O9-BHJ-549

LIFE NATURE LIBRARY

THE MAMMALS

LIFE WORLD LIBRARY

LIFE NATURE LIBRARY

TIME READING PROGRAM

THE LIFE HISTORY OF THE UNITED STATES

LIFE SCIENCE LIBRARY

INTERNATIONAL BOOK SOCIETY

GREAT AGES OF MAN

TIME-LIFE LIBRARY OF ART

TIME-LIFE LIBRARY OF AMERICA

FOODS OF THE WORLD

THIS FABULOUS CENTURY

LIFE NATURE LIBRARY

THE MAMMALS

Text by Richard Carrington
and the Editors of
TIME-LIFE BOOKS

TIME-LIFE BOOKS NEW YORK

About Richard Carrington

Richard Carrington has been fascinated by all aspects of the natural world, particularly the evolutionary destiny of man, since he was a small boy, and at 14 was the youngest Fellow of the Zoological Society of London. Planning to study science at Cambridge, he was instead swept up by World War II. He served in air-sea rescue units in the Royal Air Force, and when the war was over, embarked on a career of self-education and writing about the natural world which has preoccupied him ever since and which has made him one of the best-known English writers in the fields of natural history and anthropology. Among his books are: *A Guide to Earth History*, *Elephants*, *A Biography of the Sea* and *A Million Years of Man*. He is also the editor of the World Naturalist series of books. He is a Fellow of the Royal Anthropological Institute, a Scientific Fellow of the Zoological Society of London and a Member of the Institute of Archaeology.

ON THE COVER: An African lion dozes in the sun. Lions sleep most of the time and become active only to hunt. Their manes darken with age; from about five years on they are often known as "black-manes."

Published simultaneously in Canada.
Library of Congress catalogue card number 63-18788.
School and library distribution by Silver Burdett Company, Morristown, New Jersey.

Contents

The text for the chapters of this book was written by Richard Carrington, the picture essays by the editorial staff. The following members and departments of Time Inc. helped to produce the book: LIFE staff photographers Fritz Goro, Dmitri Kessel and George Silk; Editorial Production, Robert W. Boyd Jr.; Editorial Reference, Peter Draz; Picture Collection, Doris O'Neil; Photographic Laboratory, George Karas; TIME-LIFE News Service, Murray J. Gart.

Introduction

MANKIND'S rise to a position of dominance in life on earth has been inextricably meshed with the lives of his evolutionary classmates, the mammals. Even in the highly technological societies of today's world, men still use mammals to provide food and drink, clothing and cover, transportation and power, and a myriad of other services from chemicals to companionship. Despite this dependence upon mammals, man has confined his interests in these creatures largely to the few dozen kinds that are of direct use to him.

But what of the other thousands of species of mammals? The majority, unobtrusive creatures, are "neutrals," which man has neither interest in nor knowledge of, and the others are enemies.

Against the latter, mankind has waged a ruthless and relentless war with little success and questionable results. Shooting, trapping, gassing, poisoning, flooding and bulldozing are but a few of the techniques that have been used in attempts to eliminate certain species such as wolves and bears, but even after years of such measures, some are still "control problems"—and a few, like the coyote, have actually increased their ranges. The real victims have been the neutrals—the innocent bystanders that stumbled into traps or ate poisoned bait. In fact, the majority of the species of mammals that have become extinct in the past 2,000 years were just such neutrals, some of which were exterminated indirectly by man's activities without even his knowledge of their existence. Obviously man's interactions with mammals have been as egocentric as the pre-Copernican European's concept of the universe.

For all his technological sophistication, man is still a newcomer. It is only in the past century that he has been able to cross land, water or the air faster than a cheetah, porpoise or bat, which could claim mammalian speed records in these media for millions of years. Man's electronic sonar is far from the minute, refined echo-location mechanism of bats, and even atomic submarines cannot yet dive as deep as sperm whales. Man's technology has far to go to equal the efficiency and the variations of mammalian mechanisms. Whole areas are uninvestigated or beyond man's ken—for example, the use of odors for communication or the disease resistance of hibernators.

Above all, man is a mammal; as such, he faces the same problems of food, housing, reproduction and social behavior that other mammals do. There are many ways to solve these problems, and on the following pages in word and picture are presented, for man's edification, how mammals solve and have solved these complex problems of existence.

Richard G. Van Gelder
Chairman, Department of Mammalogy,
The American Museum of Natural History

COMING TO DRINK AT AN AFRICAN WATER HOLE, ZEBRAS MINGLE WITH WATERBUCK AND WILDEBEEST. THE KEEN EARS AND SHARP NOSES OF THE

1 The Variety of Mammals

ZEBRAS WARN THE OTHER ANIMALS OF THE APPROACH OF LIONS, WHICH FIND THE WATER HOLE CONVENIENT FOR HUNTING AS WELL AS DRINKING

When man, the dominant species on earth, looks around him, he must realize at once that he shares his home on our planet with a vast number of other living things. On a country walk he is immediately aware of the rich pageant of life of which he forms a part. In temperate or tropical regions he moves in a splendid world of trees and foliage and many-colored flowers. He hears the songs of birds, sees teeming life in every meadow and thicket and beneath the surface of every pond and stream. Even in the colder outposts of the earth, where life is more sparsely spread, he senses the immense vitality of living organisms stubbornly enduring the most barren and desolate environments.

Man's recognition of his own participation in the great drama of life varies, of course, with his imaginative capacity. Intent on the business of personal survival, he is not always excited by the wealth and variety of the living world, and his own dominance has long since given him a sense of isolation from the lower orders. There is, however, one group of creatures with which he can hardly fail to recognize his kinship. These are the mammals, the warm-blooded, generally furry and intelligent animals which form the subject of this book.

Man himself is a mammal and so also are many of the animals with whom he is most closely associated: the dogs and cats which often share his life; the cows and sheep and pigs upon which he feeds; the oxen, donkeys and horses which, until very recently, pulled his plows, carried his burdens and gave him his most effective means of transport; and the rats and mice which, even in an age when hygiene has become a fetish, still manage to appear as unwelcome guests in his home.

Quite apart from such familiar creatures, a richly varied cast of wild mammals is still spread in astonishing diversity over the face of the earth. In size they range from the 100-foot-long blue whale, which may weigh 130 tons, to the tiny shrews, whose weight may be measured in fractions of ounces. In appearance they vary from the fluttering winged bat to the sleek fish-shaped porpoise, from the long-necked giraffe to the massive elephant and from the scaly pangolin to the spiny echidna. Every one of these very different creatures is included in the one great natural group of mammals. What, if not their appearance, determines that they *are* mammals?

In the first place, all mammals belong to the important division of the animal kingdom known as the Vertebrata, or "backboned animals." But reptiles, birds, amphibians and fishes are vertebrates too. Attempting to narrow the field, we can say that all mammals have lungs and breathe atmospheric air. But so do birds and reptiles, as well as most adult amphibians. Practically every mammal gives birth to living young, but many reptiles and fish also do this. Mammals are warm-blooded, but we can say the same of birds. How then do mammals differ from their vertebrate cousins? What are the typical mammalian qualities that they share among themselves?

A most important distinction between mammals and other vertebrates is that all mammals—and only mammals—produce milk with which they feed their young. The very word mammal characterizes the group, since it is derived from the Latin *mamma*, meaning breast. It would not be true to say, however, that mammals are vertebrates typified by the possession of two or more breasts, as even some very respectable dictionaries assert. There is one primitive but highly interesting group of mammals, known as the monotremes, which lacks true mammae; the female parent secretes her milk through a number of glands which are not united, as in man and the other higher mammals, to form a nipple or teat.

Another important distinction between mammals and all other vertebrates—indeed, all other living things—is that only mammals possess true hair. Many plants are covered with processes which we call hair, as are many insects, but except in appearance these are very different structures from the hair of mammals, which grows from tiny papillae in the outer layer of the skin. This furry exterior has a valuable function for the mammals that grow it. It forms an insulating covering, helping the animal to retain its body heat. The hairs are

TEMPERATURE CONTROL AMONG REPTILES

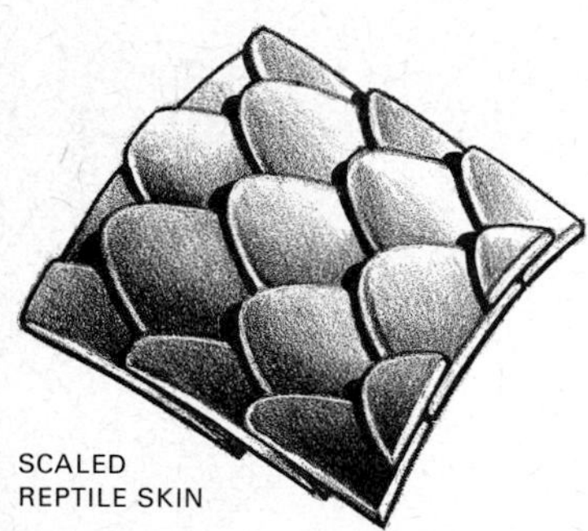

SCALED REPTILE SKIN

More primitive in many respects than mammals, reptiles have no internal temperature regulators. Their body heat is determined by their surroundings, and they control it by moving between sun and shade. They cannot cool themselves by perspiring, since their skins have no sweat glands but are dry and scaly to prevent water loss—important to many reptiles that live in hot, dry places. One advantage of cold-bloodedness is a low metabolic rate. A lizard can subsist on very little food since it is not constantly burning fuel to keep its temperature up.

also associated with glands which, by supplying an oily secretion, keep them waterproof. A hairy covering is therefore particularly important to mammals as a protection against rain and cold.

Not all mammals need the protection of a thick, furry coat. Elephants have only a very sparse covering of hair, and rhinoceroses and hippopotamuses have even less hair than elephants. In some whales, hair is usually limited to a few sensory bristles about the mouth; in others it is lacking entirely in the adult animal, although it may have appeared briefly at some stage of embryonic development. Since they live entirely in an aquatic environment, whales have evolved a protective and insulating covering formed by layers of blubber, which may be as much as 15 inches thick in some species.

Among furry mammals, the structure of the hair that forms the main body covering varies widely, forming coats as different as the soft, velvety pelage of the mole, the short, stiff covering of the horse, the curled wool of sheep and the long, thick coats of such typical fur bearers as the fox and wolverine. Quite different types of hair often grow on different parts of the body. The manes of lions and the long flowing tails of horses are made up of specialized hairs, and so are eyebrows, eyelashes and the long, sensitive whiskers which many mammals possess.

The typical fur bearer has a dense inner layer of comparatively short hair, called the undercoat, and an outer layer of longer, coarser guard hairs. (When the fur of beavers and seals is processed to make garments for human beings, the stiff guard hairs are removed.) Mammals shed their fur periodically, the old hairs dropping out and new hairs growing in. Shedding may occur seasonally once or twice a year or it may be a continuous process—as the owners of many dogs and cats can testify. In the temperate zones, coats are usually thicker in winter. Often the colors of the mammal's summer and winter coats are different as well.

Besides possessing hair and producing milk, mammals also have a number of other internal characteristics which are especially typical, though perhaps less obvious. The number of their skull bones is reduced, as compared with other vertebrates, and each half of the lower jaw consists of but a single bone. The teeth are typically differentiated and specialized. In the circulatory system, the left aortic arch forms the connection with the heart, as compared to the right aortic arch in birds. A muscular wall, or diaphragm, separates the chest cavity from the abdominal cavity. Whether their necks be long or short, or not evident at all as in the whale, nearly all mammals have seven vertebrae in the neck, the exceptions being the three-toed sloth, with nine, the tamandua, with eight, and the two-toed sloth and the manatee, each with six. And finally, among mammals the brain has developed more than in any other group.

Certain other features, although not necessarily unique, contribute to the mammals' dominance in the world. The most important of these is warm-bloodedness. This ability to maintain a stable, or nearly stable, body temperature while the temperature of the environment varies over a considerable range makes mammals both adaptable and enduring. In their capacity for heat regulation they are paralleled by the birds, but differ greatly from the cold-blooded fishes, amphibians and reptiles, whose body temperature varies with that of their surroundings. The extremes of temperature to which mammals can be exposed without a change in the temperature of their own bodies varies to some extent with different species. The arctic fox, for example, can maintain its body

TEMPERATURE CONTROL AMONG MAMMALS

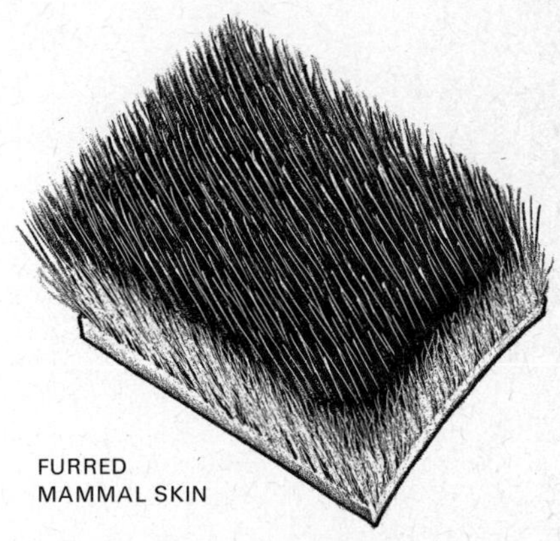

FURRED MAMMAL SKIN

In contrast to reptiles, mammals burn body fuel at a rapid rate to maintain a constant high body temperature. This permits them much greater activity than reptiles, since mammals can function in cold as well as hot weather and still keep their temperature at its proper level. The skin plays an important part in this. Horses sweat profusely over most of their bodies to cool themselves. The coyote sweats through its tongue by panting and depends on its fur to prevent heat loss in cold weather. Mammals must eat regularly to maintain their high temperatures.

heat when the thermometer reads as low as −112° F., while the white rat cannot tolerate a temperature below −13° F. Mammalian temperature also varies in some species with their degree of activity. For instance, a small bat has a higher temperature in flight than when it is at rest.

Some of the primitive mammals have appreciably less control over their temperatures than the more advanced forms. The echidna, for example, shows variations between 72° and 97° F. in its body heat, corresponding to changes in temperature of its surroundings. Animals as different as the sloth and the ground squirrel show similar changes in changing conditions. Mammals which hibernate, as do many of the cold-blooded vertebrates, may have their temperature drop to within several degrees of freezing. But these are all exceptions to the rule: as a class, mammals show the greatest and most uniform control of temperature of all the vertebrates except possibly the birds.

The mammal's insulation of fur or fat helps to retain its body heat in cold conditions. Conversely, when it is hot, mammals are cooled by the evaporation of sweat produced by special glands. Many mammals also cool themselves by panting.

A NURSING MONOTREME

The most primitive mammals are the monotremes, whose mammary glands have not concentrated into milk-producing organs, as they have in the higher mammals. The milk of the platypus, for example, seeps from a number of porelike holes in her abdomen and is lapped up by the little ones.

ANOTHER feature which has contributed significantly to the success of mammals is the intense vitality which most of them possess. In this they are not unique among vertebrates, for both fish and birds are also very lively. But these animals occupy the different environments of water and air and are not serious competitors with the mammals in their terrestrial habitat. The reptiles are a group of vertebrates with which mammals can be compared, but they are able to match the mammals in activity only when conditions are just right for them. In cold conditions reptiles become torpid and in extreme heat they die. The higher tolerance of mammals to temperature change, and their consequent ability to remain vital in much more demanding circumstances, is one of the reasons for their evolutionary success.

Certainly the most important single factor which gives mammals their superiority over other animals is the development of their brain. The mammalian brain is a complex and highly organized structure, much more advanced than that of any other animal. This development also has been made possible by the capacity for heat regulation, which has been such an advantage to mammals in other ways. The ability to maintain the complex activities of the cerebral cortex in the higher mammals, and to store memories, is very largely dependent on the ability to maintain a constant body temperature.

The brain power of mammals must be obvious to anyone who looks at them even in the most superficial way. It is as apparent in the behavior of mammals in their natural state as in the man-taught performances of dogs, seals, dolphins and apes in zoos, aquariums and circuses. The cooperative hunting of wolves and killer whales, the careful nurturing of the young by mammalian parents, the social behavior of chimpanzees, baboons and other apes and monkeys are all evidence of a high degree of intelligence. A number of the primates even appear to have some ability to solve problems by deductive reasoning, as experiments with chimpanzees amply demonstrate. The complexification of the brain has, of course, reached its highest point so far in the extraordinary mammal, man, and is entirely responsible for the richness and diversity of his emotional and intellectual life.

In spite of their present dominance in the world, mammals constitute a very small class numerically when compared with many of the other animal groups.

Of insects alone, more than three quarters of a million different species have been described and these by no means exhaust the list, for many new species and subspecies are discovered every year. In contrast, all the vertebrate classes together total less than 44,000 living species. Of these, at least 20,000 are fish, 8,600 are birds, 6,000 are reptiles and about 3,000 are amphibians. The mammals total about 4,300 species and are thus less numerous than any other vertebrate class except the amphibians.

The naming of the various types of organisms, including the mammals, was undertaken in the 18th Century by the great Swedish botanist Linnaeus. For the 10th edition of his *Systema naturae*, published in 1758, he listed only 86 species of mammals, which he placed in eight different subdivisions, or orders. He based his classification on obvious external characteristics, much as a librarian might group books by putting all oversized red books together, all small green books together and so on, regardless of the subject matter and author. However, Linnaeus did show a great deal of insight for his time. He had very little concrete knowledge to guide him. In the 12th edition of his work, published in 1766, he used a somewhat more complex classification, listing all his mammalian groups under three principal divisions: the Unguiculata, or mammals with claws and nails; the Ungulata, or mammals with hoofs; and the Mutica, or mammals without either claws or hoofs, such as whales.

In the following century, many systems and categories for classifying mammals were used, but practically all continued to utilize the principle of separating mammals according to external differences. However, when the fossil record began to be used as a key to the ancestral lines of living animals and the theory of evolution gained acceptance, the emphasis of classification shifted and mere cataloguing of animals changed to a system which attempted to show their true relationships and origins by reference to anatomical criteria.

UNDER this system, the living members of the class Mammalia are today divided into three main subclasses, according to differences in their anatomy and the manner in which they bear their young. First are the monotremes, or egg-laying mammals, of which there are only two families. Second are the marsupials, or mammals with pouches for carrying their young, which are comparatively undeveloped, even embryonic in appearance, at birth. Third, and by far the largest group, are the placentals, mammals whose young grow and develop within the mother's body, nourished by means of an organ known as the placenta, which forms a connecting link with her own blood stream. These three major divisions are thought to have developed very early in mammalian history, each of them evolving thereafter quite independently of the others.

But these three main divisions are just the beginning. Living mammals are further divided into 18 smaller groups or orders. Subdivisions of each order are also made—families, genera, species and so on—the various mammals being grouped according to their degree of evolutionary kinship. In addition to any popular name or names it may have, each species of animal known to zoologists is given a scientific name intended to identify it beyond any shadow of doubt.

The study of animal relationships and phylogeny is complicated by superficial likenesses between quite different kinds of animals—fish and porpoises, to take an obvious example. Many mammals of quite different origins have acquired very similar adaptations under the influence of similar surroundings or ways of life, a process known as convergent evolution. Thus the echidna, the hedgehog and the porcupine have all evolved quills, but quite independently of each other.

A NURSING MARSUPIAL

More advanced are the marsupials such as the opossum shown here. They have true nipples, but these are located inside a pouch, or marsupium, to which their comparatively unformed babies crawl at birth. There they live for several months until they are much larger and more developed.

SIMILAR SKULLS: DIFFERENT BODIES

WEASEL

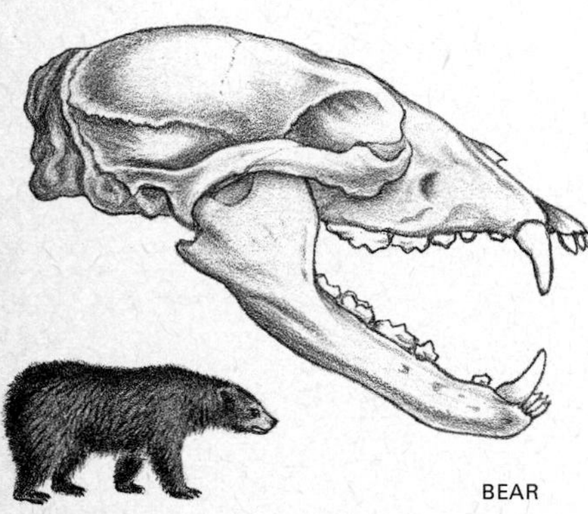

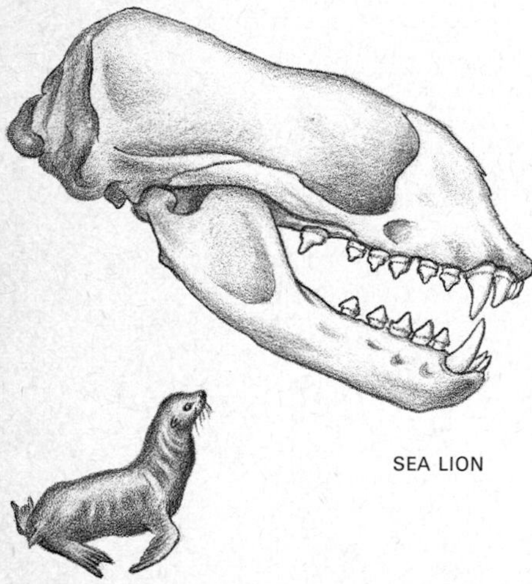

The appearance of mammals as a guide to the closeness of their relationship is often deceiving. The weasel, the bear and the sea lion, though they have no external resemblance, are all carnivores. This is shown by an examination of their skulls. Each has the powerful lower jaw and the sharp, well-developed canines of a hunting animal—although there are slight modifications reflecting different eating habits. The seal's molars, for example, are pointed to help it hold fish, whereas the omnivorous bear's are flatter.

Superficially they resemble one another, but actually each is about as distant in relationship from the others as it is possible for a mammal to be. Likewise, the little flying squirrels of North America and some of the flying possums, or sugar gliders, of Australia are so similar in general appearance that at first glance they might be taken for the same species. The first, however, are placental mammals and the second marsupials, and their evolution has been separate and distinct for many millions of years.

Even the study of the geographical distribution of mammals is full of pitfalls for the student. Some groups—the Australian marsupials and the lemurs of Madagascar, for example, have developed in relative isolation. Others, such as the horses and camels, originated on one continent, then left their ancestral home and spread to other continents by land bridges which may have subsequently disappeared.

THE system by which individual kinds of mammals are scientifically named within the large categories can be seen by taking a familiar example, the wolf. First of all, the wolf belongs to the class Mammalia. Then it falls in a group made up of the placental mammals, and is further separated into the order Carnivora, or meat-eating mammals. To distinguish it from such other meat eaters as cats, weasels and the like, it is placed in the family Canidae, that of the dog-like carnivores. Together with various other closely related species, it is included in the genus *Canis*, which separates it from such closely allied groups as the foxes and the bush dogs. The specific name of the wolf is *Canis lupus*, distinguishing it from all near relatives, such as the coyote *(Canis latrans)* and the domestic dog *(Canis familiaris)*.

The scientific names of mammals will not be used much in this book, although such use sometimes may be necessary. The reader should realize that these names do not belong to some secret language. They are really only the equivalents of the Christian names and surnames of a person as written in reverse order in the telephone directory, e.g., Smith, Albert, or Brown, Charles. It is not difficult to understand how convenient this system of labeling is. Not only does it give a good idea of the relationship of one animal to its nearest kin, but it also enables scientists and others to refer to animals in writing and conversation far more accurately than by using their popular names, which are often very imprecise and, of course, vary from language to language and from region to region. The name gopher, for example, means a certain kind of turtle to many citizens in the southern states, a striped ground squirrel to many Midwesterners, and to still others an entirely different burrowing rodent with external cheek pouches.

The time has now come to introduce some of the star members of the mammalian cast, order by order, for a knowledge of the dramatis personae is essential to a meaningful study of mammals. The following brief account of the three main groups and some of the more important orders, together with a word on relationships, gives the indispensable key to the story told in later chapters.

The monotremes, the only order in the first of the three major mammalian groups, are the most primitive living mammals. Their shoulder girdles are curiously reptilian and they have but a single external opening for the elimination of all body wastes as well as for reproductive functions. The females lay eggs, as birds and reptiles do. Probably isolated from a very early period when mammals were still in the process of evolving from reptiles, the monotremes emerged as a wholly separate line. There are only three living genera—the well-known duckbill, or platypus, and the two kinds of echidnas, or spiny anteaters. All three are limited to Australasia.

The second great group of mammals is also composed of only one order, the Marsupialia, or pouched mammals. These are restricted to Australasia, where they have evolved into a great number of widely different forms, and to the Americas, where many species of opossums and a few "opossum-rats" still flourish. Marsupials show an advance over the monotremes in their method of reproduction, but nevertheless follow a very specialized and unique procedure of their own. Young marsupials do not remain for nearly such a long period in the uterus, or womb, of the mother as do the young of many higher mammals. Born in a very undeveloped condition, they crawl directly into the marsupium, or pouch, which gives the group its name. So unready is the newly born marsupial to deal with the problems of living that it remains attached to the mother's nipple for many weeks as it develops. A few species of marsupials do not have enclosing pouches, but their exposed young remain attached to the mother's nipples in the same way.

The kangaroo is the most familiar of the pouched mammals. There are many species, varying in size from little foot-high wallabies and rat kangaroos to the red kangaroo, which on its hind feet stands taller than the average man. Most of them are noted for their jumping abilities, but some species are primarily arboreal. Another well-known marsupial is the koala, which looks something like a benign Teddy bear and eats only the leaves and shoots of certain species of eucalyptus trees. It is seldom seen outside of Australia, however, because rigid protective laws now forbid its exportation.

Besides these, there are many other kinds of marsupials which are not so well known. Some of them have made a wide variety of adaptations to many different ways of life, and there are terrestrial, arboreal, burrowing and gliding forms. In occupying all these environments, they often parallel the forms taken by many placental mammals. Marsupial "rats" and "mice" resemble rodents. The Tasmanian devil, the Tasmanian "wolf," and the strange marsupial "cats" all parallel placental carnivores. There is a marsupial "mole" and a marsupial "anteater." Phalangers and sugar gliders resemble squirrels, and the wombat is something like a huge groundhog. All of these very distinctive forms differ from placental mammals not only in their method of bearing young, but in their anatomy. Their brains still retain many reptilian characteristics and both male and female have two bones known as the marsupial bones attached to the pelvis; the female also has two separate vaginal canals and uteri.

All of the other living mammals in the world belong to the third group, that of the placental mammals, named for that special organ, the placenta, which has been such an important factor in determining their evolutionary success. Placenta literally means "flat cake," and the organ is so named from its characteristic shape in humans. It is essentially a development of membranes which, in the reptilian ancestors of the mammals, surrounded the growing embryo within the egg. In placental mammals these membranes have become fused to the walls of the womb, enabling the fetus to draw nourishment directly from the body of the mother instead of relying on the limited supply of food contained within the egg itself. The great advantage of this procedure is that the young animal can remain for a much longer period within the body of the mother, thus allowing considerably more time for its complicated brain and body mechanisms to mature in a thoroughly protected environment.

DIFFERENT SKULLS: SIMILAR BODIES

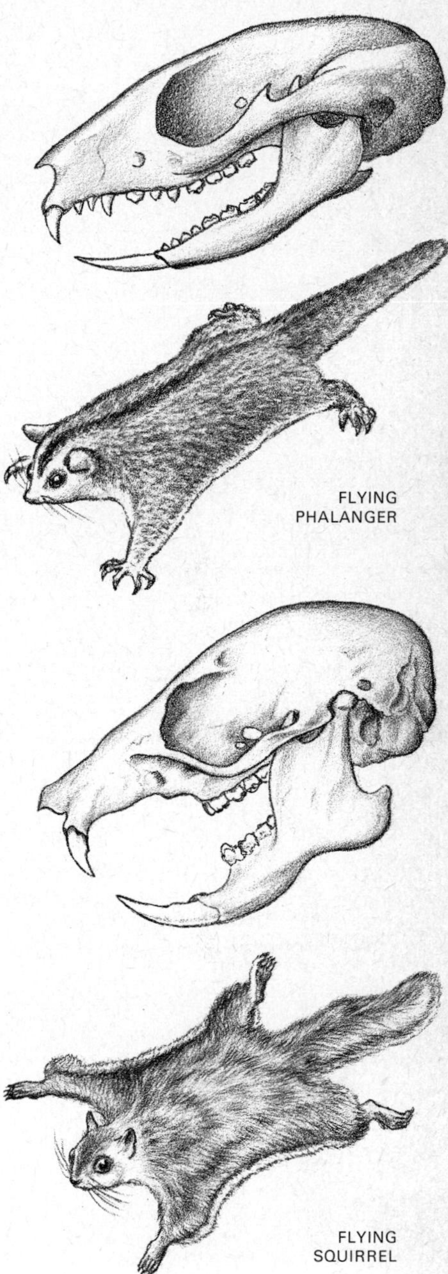

Other animals, despite a very close surface resemblance, may not be closely related at all. These two nocturnal, arboreal, gliding mammals have come to look like one another from very different evolutionary beginnings. The flying phalanger is a marsupial, and the flying squirrel a rodent. Beneath their surface similarities are fundamental skeletal differences. The phalanger's skull shows the small, pointed teeth of an insect eater, while the squirrel (a nut and seed eater) has gnawing incisors and grinding molars.

The placentals, because of their diversity, are divided into 16 different orders, which together make up the great majority of the more than a thousand genera (including some 4,300 species) of mammals. If a study of mammalian life is to be meaningful, a general picture of the characteristics of these orders and the way they resemble and differ from one another is the necessary starting point. Here, then, is the placental cast.

The order Dermoptera (literally skin-wings) is represented by only one living genus. This is the so-called flying lemur, or colugo, a nocturnal mammal whose range is restricted to the tropical forests of Southeast Asia and the adjacent islands. It lives entirely in the trees, and its elongated limbs are connected by a membranous skin which enables it to glide from bough to bough.

The living members of the order Insectivora, or insect eaters, although still not a large group, are more diversified. These small mammals, all short-legged except for the elephant shrews, include the shrews, moles and hedgehogs. The shrews have a special interest for the student of evolution because they may resemble the animals from which many major orders of mammals developed.

The Chiroptera (literally hand-wings), or bats, are fairly closely related to the flying lemurs and insectivores. They are a very specialized group and the only mammals to have achieved true flight. After the rodents, they are also the largest order, comprising no fewer than 17 families represented by some 900 species.

THE aardvark (from two Dutch words meaning earth pig) is the only living representative of the order Tubulidentata and has a range restricted to Africa south of the Sahara. It has a long and fairly slender snout, a sticky tongue and strong digging claws—all admirably adapted for raiding anthills and termite nests. The strange tube-shaped and rootless teeth which give the order Tubulidentata its name seem to have no obvious function in the aardvark and are probably vestiges of an ancestral form with a quite different way of life.

Another odd group are the pangolins, comprised within the order Pholidota. These mammals, which are covered with overlapping horny plates instead of hair, are able to protect themselves by rolling up; in fact, their popular name comes from the Malay word *peng-goling*, meaning "roller." Various species of pangolins occur in Africa and Southeast Asia. Like the aardvark, they feed on ants and termites.

Both the aardvarks and the pangolins were once grouped with the mammalian order known as the Edentata, or toothless ones, but were later regarded as being so distinct in structure that they were separated from the group. The true edentates living today are of three kinds: the armadillos, the anteaters and the sloths. Superficially these animals look very different, but they are all characterized by either lack of teeth or a very poorly developed dentition, and a study of their fossil forms shows that they can probably trace back their origin to a common ancestor.

The armadillos resemble the pangolins in having the upper part of the body covered with protective plates, although these have evolved in a different way. In spite of being classified with the toothless ones, the armadillos do possess teeth, which vary in number from 28 to 100 in different species, but they are very weak and ill suited for biting and chewing. By contrast, the anteaters from Central and South America are typical edentates in that they have no teeth at all. The long claws, well adapted for digging in anthills and termite mounds, make walking difficult, so they are turned inward and the animal carries its weight on the outside of the feet. The sloths, which come from the same region, are all arboreal; they make their way upside down among the branches, hanging by their strong, curved claws.

The rodents (order Rodentia) are the most richly represented of all the mammalian orders. In fact, between a third and a half of all the living land mammals come within the group. They are mostly small animals with a high rate of reproduction, and form the main item in the diet of the smaller predators. Their name comes from the Latin verb *rodere*, to gnaw, and all rodents are characterized by their sharp chisel-shaped incisors, or gnawing teeth. The rodents with which everyone is most familiar are the various species of rats and mice. Other well-known members of the group are the tree squirrels, of which there are some 200 species distributed in every part of the world except Australia, Madagascar, Antarctica and certain isolated regions in the north. Closely related to these, although ground-dwelling rather than arboreal in habit, are the marmots, found in many parts of Europe, Asia and North America. The largest of all rodents is the capybara, a kind of outsize guinea pig from South America, which may reach a length of over three feet.

The hares and rabbits of the order Lagomorpha (literally, hare-shaped) are distinguished from true rodents by having two pairs of upper incisor teeth instead of one, and are also characterized by their long ears and by having the hind limbs considerably more developed than the forelimbs, which makes them very efficient runners. However, some members of the order, the pikas, have fore and hind limbs of about equal length and have short, broad ears. The teeth differences are therefore important in separating lagomorphs from rodents.

The Carnivora, or flesh eaters, are almost as diversified as the rodents. The living families of carnivores are: the cats; the dogs; the hyenas; the bears; the raccoons, coatis and pandas; the martens, badgers, skunks, otters and their kin; the civets and mongooses; the seals; the sea lions; and the walruses.

THE cat family includes a wide range of highly efficient carnivores, ranging from the lion and tiger to a number of smaller species, which nevertheless have a very similar structure. The teeth of cats are admirably designed for stabbing, biting and slicing and they usually hunt by careful stalking, followed by a sudden rush on the quarry. The dogs are likewise a well-diversified group, but their pattern of survival is different from that of the cats. Dogs are on the whole more sociable and commonly live and hunt in packs. The dog family also contains a number of forms, such as jackals, which lack the aggressive instincts typical of most carnivores and feed mainly on carrion. Bears are not so typically carnivorous; they readily eat honey, berries and other vegetable food.

The aquatic carnivores, represented by the seals and their kin, are highly specialized for life in the sea and their limbs have been modified into flippers well suited for propulsion in the water. The giant of the group, which is among the largest of all mammals, is the elephant seal. A large bull may attain a length of 18 feet and a weight of more than three tons. Its name is derived not only from its size, but from the trunklike snout which develops in mature males and which may be over two feet long.

Still more highly adapted for marine life than the seals are the whales and dolphins of the order Cetacea. In fact, although they are warm-blooded creatures which suckle their young, they are often mistaken for fish. This is not surprising, for they differ from most mammals in having little or no external hair and in having heads, trunks and tails that merge into one another to give them a typically fishlike shape.

ODD AND EVEN TOES

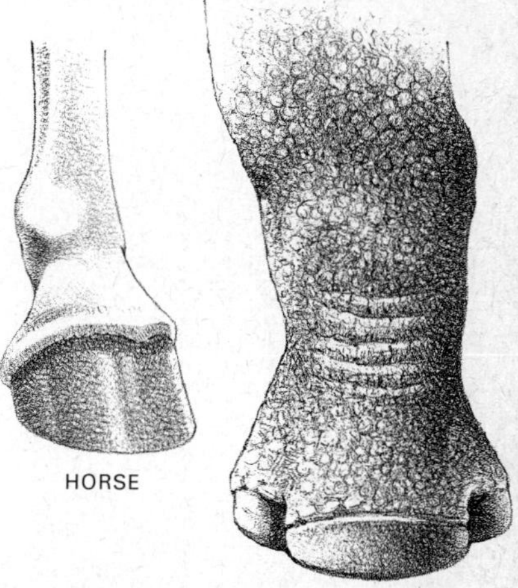

The hoofed animals, or ungulates, started out with five toes, but for greater efficiency in walking and running, the number has gradually become reduced. One group has an odd number of toes; like the rhinoceros, which has three, or the horse, which now has only one. The hoof of the horse is actually the nail of its middle toe.

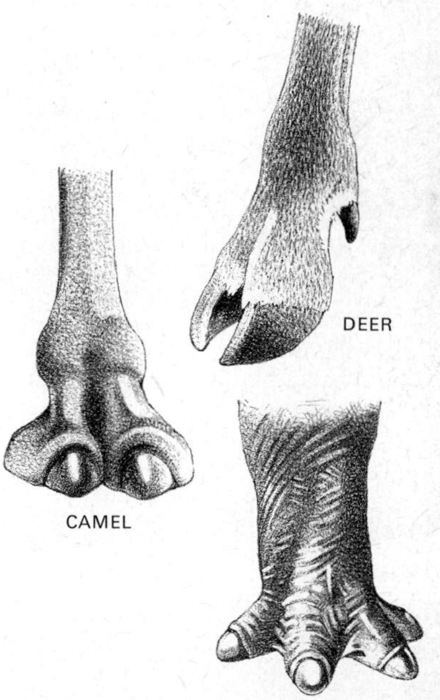

The cloven hoofs of even-toed ungulates, such as pigs, cattle and deer, represent the evolutionary transformation of the third and fourth toes, now sheathed in keratin. Not all the members of this group actually have hoofs. Two exceptions are the four-toed hippopotamus and the camel, whose feet are padded for walking on soft sand.

The three next orders of mammals, although dissimilar in appearance and habits, are fairly closely related. The hyraxes (order Hyracoidea) are small, active creatures from Africa and the Middle East. The two main forms live respectively in burrows and in trees and have a superficial resemblance to woodchucks. The manatees and dugongs of the order Sirenia are, by contrast, large, sluggish, aquatic mammals inhabiting the estuaries and coastal waters of the tropics. Elephants (order Proboscidea) are too well known to need introduction, although it is not always remembered that there are two quite distinct forms—the big-eared, concave-backed African genus and the small-eared, convex-backed Asiatic genus.

The hoofed mammals are divided into two orders having respectively an odd and even number of toes. Those with an odd number are known scientifically as Perissodactyla; those with an even number, Artiodactyla. More generally, and less exactly, both orders are grouped together and are known as the Ungulata, from the Latin *ungula*, meaning a hoof or claw. The odd-toed ungulates include three main groups of living mammals: the horses, the tapirs and the rhinoceroses. The tapirs, whose range is limited to tropical America and Southeast Asia, are very reminiscent of the stock from which all the living odd-toed ungulates are descended, but are now usually found in the vicinity of water, to which they will take with great readiness if danger threatens. The rhinoceroses, by contrast, are much more specialized. There are two forms in Africa and three in Asia, all characterized by exceptionally thick skins and the presence of a varying number of "horns" on their snouts. These horns are of a very special type, however, consisting of a rigid pyramid of closely impacted hair.

The even-toed ungulates are a much more diverse group than their odd-toed cousins. These are the so-called cloven-hoofed mammals, although in reality the cleft is simply the gap between two central and quite distinct digits. Nearly all of the domestic animals, which are so familiar to us, such as cattle, sheep and pigs, come within the order. Other artiodactyls are the camels and llamas, the hippopotamus, the giraffe, the okapis, the antelopes and gazelles and the various species of deer.

THE most advanced of all the mammalian orders is the primates, which includes monkeys, apes—and man. Although their name is derived from the Latin *primus*, meaning first, this does not mean that they were the first to evolve, but simply that they are the first in order of importance. The most primitive living primates are little creatures known as tree shrews, whose range is restricted to Southeast Asia. The island of Madagascar off Southeast Africa is the main home of the shy, usually nocturnal primates known as lemurs. Their name comes from the Latin *lemures*, meaning spirits of the dead, and they do indeed move about in the dense jungle like ghosts. But much more familiar to most people than any of these primates are the monkeys and the great apes. Monkeys occur in both the Old and New Worlds and include such ground-dwelling forms as the baboons, as well as a much larger number of arboreal species. The four great anthropoid apes—the chimpanzee, the gorilla, the orangutan and the gibbons—are our own nearest living relatives in the Animal Kingdom.

Many aspects of the lives of primates as well as of other members of the diversified mammalian cast will be dealt with later in this book. Among these is a problem of paramount interest: Where did all this rich array of mammals come from; how did they evolve into their present forms; and what are the scientific laws which may explain why they live where they do?

A MASKED SHREW, ONE OF THE WORLD'S TINIEST MAMMALS, PEERS OVER A MAN'S FOREFINGER. IT MEASURES THREE INCHES, TAIL AND ALL

The Many Mammal Forms

The contrast between a shrew weighing a tenth of an ounce and a 130-ton whale symbolizes the enormous range of mammalian life. Though the class of mammals includes comparatively few species, they are very diversified in their habits and habitats. Mammals are found everywhere on the earth's surface—desert, forest, polar ice-cap, mountain peak—and also at sea, in the air and underground.

Mammalian Orders

All the 4,287 known living species of mammals fall into one or another of the 18 orders shown here, each with its scientific name under it in large type, as in Monotremata, Rodentia, etc. The common name of the individual animal representing the order is in small type. In some instances more than one animal is shown, to reflect the wide variety of types within that order.

Some orders have been grouped together on the same sections of tinted background to show that they are more closely related to each other than to other orders—like the Artiodactyla (even-toed ungulates) and the odd-toed Perissodactyla. Doubtful relationships are indicated by dotted lines. This arrangement, based on structural similarity and fossil evidence rather than appearance, reveals some unexpected relationships—of elephant to hyrax, for example. More surprising, perhaps, men are more closely related to shrews than to most other orders.

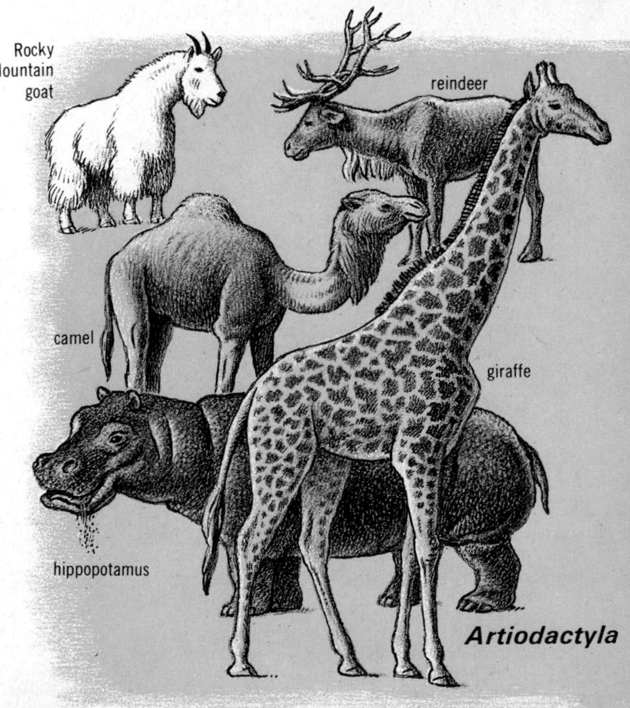

koala
opossum
kangaroo
Marsupialia
sloth
anteater
armadillo
Edentata
pangolin
Pholidota

bat
colugo
Dermoptera
Chiroptera
tree shrew
chimpanzee
shrew
mole
Insectivora
monkey
man
lemur
Primates

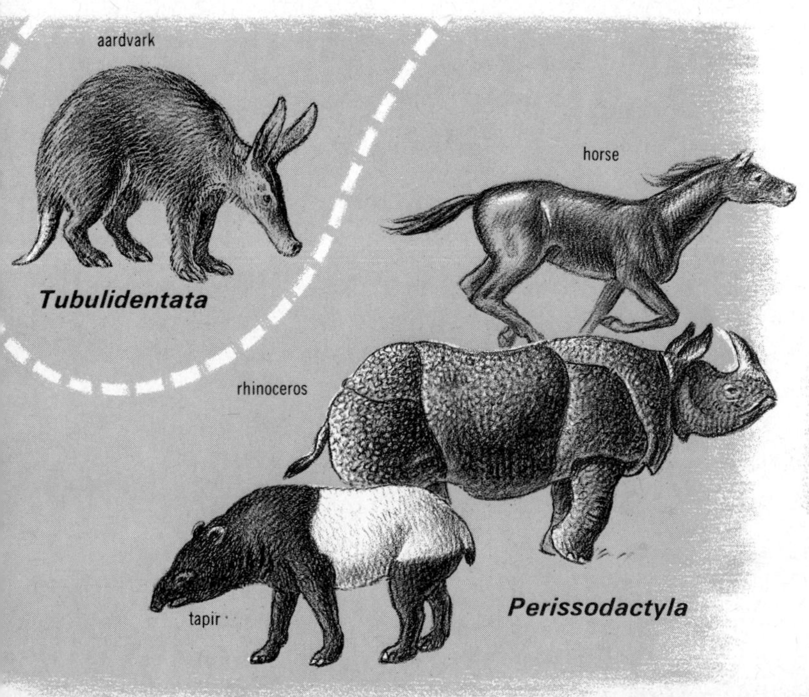
aardvark
Tubulidentata
horse
rhinoceros
tapir
Perissodactyla

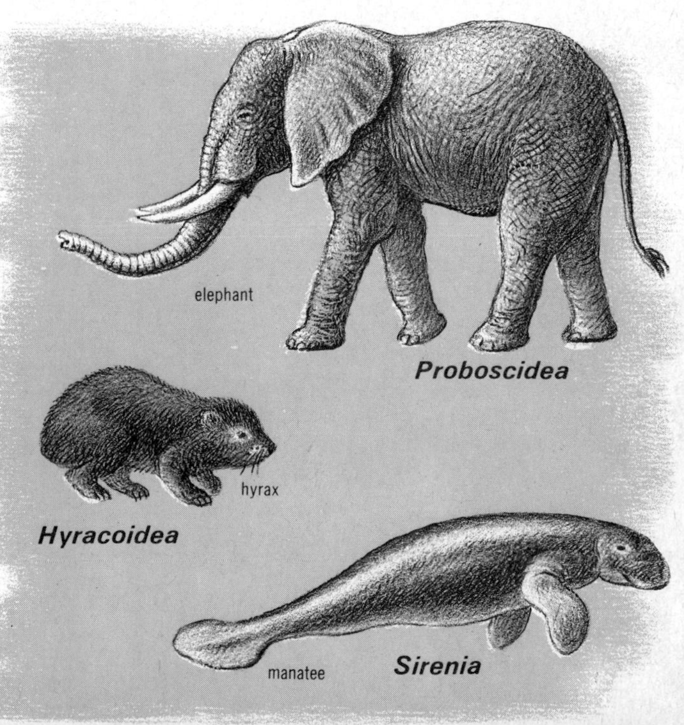
elephant
Proboscidea
hyrax
Hyracoidea
manatee
Sirenia

How Abundant Are Mammals As a Class?

Although mammals are generally considered to be the dominant and probably most diversified class of living vertebrates, they are far from being the most numerous. If the total numbers of species for all the major animal groups are compared, the mammals come out almost at the bottom. The sizes of the different creatures in this drawing illustrate this point. At the left is a very small frog, representing 3,000 living species of amphibians. Then come the other vertebrate classes in order of increasing number of species: the mammals, reptiles, birds and fishes. The large snail next in line represents the invertebrates: all the one-celled animals, all the worms, clams, lobsters, spiders—everything else, in short, except the insects. Strictly speaking the insects should be lumped with the other invertebrates, but there are so many of them—more different species than in all the other groups put together—that they have been represented separately here by the huge butterfly at the right.

INSECTS
800,000

What Are the Commonest Mammals?

With mammals placed in proper numerical perspective vis-à-vis other animals, what about the relative abundance of the different mammals themselves? This second series of drawings illustrates that point. Counting actual numbers of animals is far more difficult than numbers of species. The only way it can be done is to take a small sample area and laboriously count every nose in it. This has been done many times in different parts of the world. While results vary widely depending on the terrain and the time of year, nevertheless in most areas the rodents turn out to have by far the largest populations. The five mammals pictured here show what lives on 250 acres of sagebrush country in the western U.S., based on a study of a 2.5-acre sample area. They illustrate two general principles: 1) carnivores (in this case, badgers) tend to be far less numerous than the animals they eat; 2) the smaller the animal, the larger its population can be in a given area.

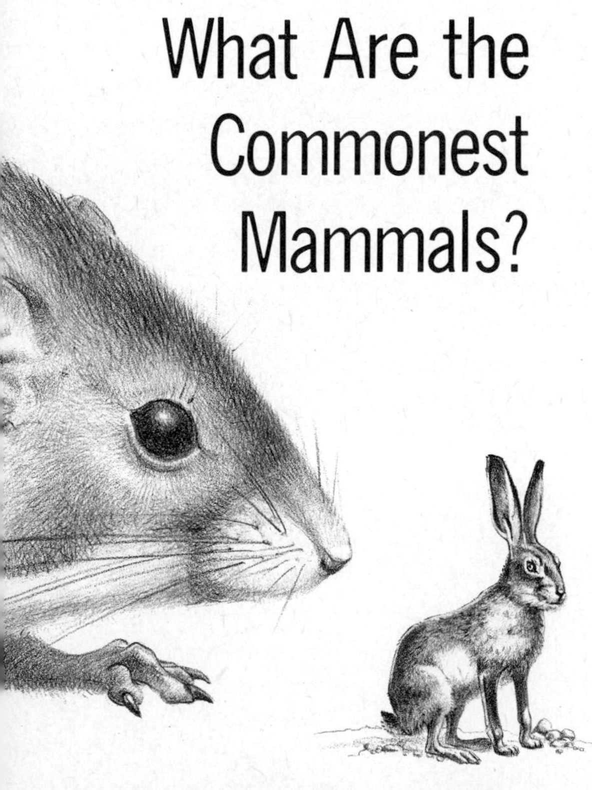

RODENTS
5,770

RABBITS
60

BADGERS
30

PRONGHORNS
10

BATS
8

A CLOUD OF BATS STREAMS FROM A LIMESTONE CAVE NEAR BRAUNFELS, TEXAS. THIS COLONY NUMBERS ABOUT EIGHT MILLION INDIVIDUALS

Fliers and Leapers

Among the mammals are several groups that do much of their traveling through the air—by flying, gliding or leaping. True flight is achieved only by the bats. Flying squirrels, flying lemurs and flying phalangers actually glide rather than fly, sailing on flaps of skin stretched between their front and back limbs. Though functionally similar, these three animals are not related: the squirrel is a rodent; the phalanger a marsupial; and the flying lemur has an order, the Dermoptera, all to itself.

The nonfliers include, in addition to many leaping monkeys, other tree dwellers, like the tropical kinkajou, southern relative of the raccoon, which swings from branch to branch by its prehensile tail.

AERIAL ACROBATICS are practiced by a group of squirrel monkeys. A New World species, they travel through the forest in groups of several hundred, hurling themselves through the air for distances of 20 feet and, like those shown above, apparently disdaining to look where they are heading. They sometimes leap up from the tops of trees in an effort to catch flying insects.

A SCHOOL OF DOLPHINS churns the waters in the Gulf of California. Though they look like fish, dolphins are true mammals; they are warm-blooded, breathe air and nurse their young. Recent studies of their learning ability suggest that they are extremely intelligent. Dolphins are found in most waters of the world. Highly sociable, they range in size from six to 13 feet.

A CROWD OF WALRUSES jams a narrow beach in summer in the Bering Sea. Normally brownish in color, these mammals get hot when they lie in the sun, and turn a rich pink from the dilation of surface blood vessels. In winter they live on the edges of the pack ice; they need access to open water in order to dive to the bottom for shellfish, which they dig up with their tusks.

SURVIVING IN THE DESERT, asses turn tail to a Sahara sandstorm, in obedience to age-old protective habits inherited from their wild ancestors. These asses escaped from domestication and resumed the hardy life of their African forebears.

DWELLERS OF THE ARCTIC ICE, two female polar bears and their three offspring hunt together. A polar bear mother keeps her cubs with her till they are about two years old, and sometimes allows them to cling to her tail while she is swimming.

A FOREST HUNTER, the bobcat preys on mice, rabbits and birds. It does most of its work at night and is rarely seen in daylight. Bobcats are very strong for their size and have vicious tempers. They look like large house cats, but have bigger ears, stubby tails and long, thick cheek whiskers.

CAUGHT IN A SHAFT OF SUNLIGHT, two white-tailed fawns refresh themselves at a Wisconsin lake. They still show the white spots on back and flanks that mark the first four or five months of life. With few defenses but alertness and speed, white-tails can run as fast as 50 miles an hour.

A HERD OF BISON rumbles across the grassland of the National Bison Range in western Montana. Bison are unpredictable animals, and the term "to buffalo" comes from the ease with which hunters could bewilder them and trigger them into mass stampedes. The Plains Indians used this characteristic to run them over cliffs, where they would be killed by the thousands.

As many as 60 million bison once roamed North America, perhaps the greatest population of a single large mammal in the earth's history. Hunted almost to extinction by 1900, bison herds today must be kept thinned to prevent overgrazing. There are now about 30,000 in the United States and Canada. Buffalo skulls and bones can still be found on the Western plains.

THE WHITE RHINO, suggestive of one of the extinct, tanklike animals of the prehistoric past, may be headed for extinction itself. Preserves have been established for it in Africa and specimens are also being sent to zoos in an attempt to ensure its survival.

2

Mammalian Evolution

Little more than a century ago, few people realized that the diverse array of mammals we have just described were not only related to one another but to all other living things. Religion taught that each individual type of animal had been created by God to fulfill a special role in the world. The idea that the mighty elephant, the tiny shrew, the lithe and graceful panther, the monkeys, apes and even man were in a very real sense cousins would have been regarded at best as a mad delusion and at worst as blasphemy. Yet we now know beyond a doubt that all these creatures can trace their ancestry back to a common stock.

The revelation of this fact is, of course, due to the discovery of the principles of organic evolution. The idea of the evolution of all life was discussed by the ancient Greeks, but after them it was forgotten for more than 2,000 years and men's minds were preoccupied with more magical interpretations of nature. It was not until the middle of the 18th Century that the idea was reborn, this time with new vitality. A century later, in 1859, Charles Darwin's *On the Origin of Species by Means of Natural Selection* was published. This classic book presented the story of evolution so clearly that it could no longer be rationally denied, and later work has served only to confirm its basic truth.

Very briefly, the theory of evolution comprises the idea that all living things belong to one great family and that later and more complex forms have developed from simpler forms that preceded them. The various members of this family became differentiated over many millions of years by the process known as "natural selection." This process can operate because individual organisms from time to time produce definite heritable variations, known as "mutations," in the germ cells that give rise to the next generation. Thus, in any given environment, there will be individuals who, through favorable mutation, have become better adapted to their way of life than their fellows. These individuals will be more likely to remain alive and reproduce themselves, and nature can therefore be said to have "selected" that type for survival from among its less well-equipped rivals. This process is repeated in each generation, with different qualities selected in different environments. Thus different "species" are eventually established, each with its own adaptations to its particular circumstances.

THE SPIRAL OF TIME

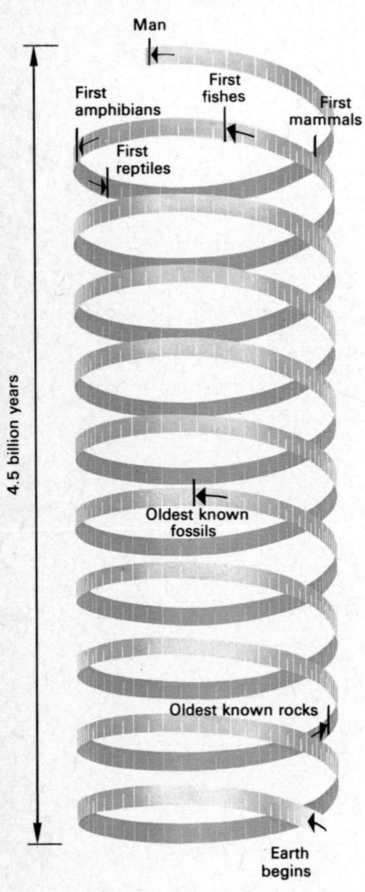

The spiraling tape depicted here represents four and a half billion years of earth history, starting at bottom with the formation of the planet and proceeding upward to the present. Marked on the tape in their appropriate places are the high points in the evolution of life, revealing the relative newness of the mammals as a group and ending with man, whose million or so years of existence are the merest sliver at the top of the coil. The vertical lines on the tape mark approximately five-million-year intervals.

THE history of the earth is very long, at least 4.5 billion years, according to the findings of the latest research. However, no more than half of this immense span of time has been characterized by the evolution of living organisms. Through chemical reactions on the shores of the very early rivers or seas, the first tiny one-celled organisms known as "protistans" probably developed. As the generations passed, life increased in variety and complexity, and higher and higher kinds of organisms evolved. First there were soft-bodied creatures such as sponges and jellyfish, then creatures with protective shells. After these came a sequence of backboned animals, or "vertebrates," represented in ascending order by fishes, amphibians, reptiles and, finally, mammals and birds. The full story of this wonderful process and how it has been pieced together from the study of fossils is told in another book in this series, *Evolution*, by Ruth Moore.

Here, where we are concerned only with the mammals, our tale begins some 180 million years ago. At that remote time, which is yet recent when we consider the total age of the earth, our planet was dominated by reptiles. Giant dinosaurs ranged over the land, huge aquatic reptiles known as ichthyosaurs and plesiosaurs swam in the seas, and weird flying reptiles known as pterosaurs took to the air. These last had membranous "wings" comparable in function, though not in the details of their structure, to those of living bats.

What is often hard to realize is that all mammals living today, including all humans, are direct descendants of reptiles that lived in this ancient period. Yet it is a fact—and this fact gives us an added interest in considering the question: What were these ancient ancestors of the mammals like?

Evolution works by infinitely slow stages, so there is no one point where we can say that, as if at the blowing of a trumpet, mammals were born from the parent reptile stock. An important early approach to mammalian structure was taken by lizardlike creatures known as pelycosaurs, which date back 280 million years or more—long before the appearance of true mammals. These were represented by both meat-eating and vegetarian forms, some of which were typified by great sail-like structures running the length of their backs. But instead of the uniform rows of teeth of other reptiles, many pelycosaurs had front teeth somewhat like mammalian incisors. Behind these were large canines, then grinding cheek teeth comparable to a mammal's molars and premolars.

Related to the pelycosaurs was a group of even more mammal-like reptiles called therapsids, most of which were aggressive meat eaters. These had skulls and teeth which in many ways were quite similar to those of mammals, and limbs which were shifting from the sprawling "out-to-the-side" position of early amphibian and some land-dwelling reptiles to the fore-and-aft position of typical mammals. One of the later therapsids, *Kannemeyeria*, had a strange beak-like snout. Another, called *Cynognathus* (dog jaw), was a powerful carnivore with teeth very much like those of true mammals.

The structure of the teeth, among other features, shows that pelycosaurs and therapsids, although not necessarily the direct ancestors of mammals, may certainly be regarded as their ancient uncles and aunts. The fossil record does not tell us whether therapsids were warm-blooded, whether they had hair instead of scales and whether they nursed their young. But judging from the progressive modifications of their hard parts, they may possibly have been developing these typically mammalian characteristics.

Fossils, unfortunately, reveal very little about the creatures which we consider the first true mammals. From the few remains which have been discovered—mainly teeth and jaws—we know that they were mostly tiny animals no bigger than rats and mice. They exploited different ways of life from those practiced by the reptiles. Some of them hunted the insects that dwelt in the undergrowth of tropical jungles, while others took to the trees to avoid direct competition with their ground-dwelling contemporaries. In the unstable environment of the treetops, which makes such rigorous demands on the coordination of the muscles controlling locomotion, these ancient ancestors of monkeys, apes and men began to develop the complex brains that still distinguish the primates today.

Now all these events were occurring at a time when reptiles still dominated the earth. It was not until some 60 million years ago that the pattern of life changed and the true mammalian descendants of the mammal-like reptiles finally began to assert their pre-eminence. For reasons which are still not fully understood, almost all the great reptiles which had ruled the earth for some 200 million years became extinct.

One of the main causes of the mass extinction was probably a radical change in climate, related to geological and cosmological events. The ruling reptiles, with their limited tolerance of external temperatures and their reliance on specialized types of food which no longer flourished in their former abundance, were ruthlessly eliminated. Unable to adapt, they perished. The disappearance of these formerly dominant creatures created a kind of biological vacuum, which the more adaptable mammals were quick to exploit. And with their internal thermostats, more advanced brains, and an improved method of bearing and raising their young, they were able to exploit it very efficiently indeed.

The next 60 million-odd years of earth history have been aptly termed the Age of Mammals—the great period of mammalian expansion and differentiation when all the creatures mentioned in the previous chapter went through the major phases of their evolution and became established, with suitable physical and mental specializations, in the different regions they occupy today. In a sense we still live in the Age of Mammals, although the past million years in particular have been a period of rapid decline for the group as a whole. This has been attended by the spectacular rise of one particular mammal, man, whose evolving mind has enabled him to establish a position of unchallenged supremacy over his mammalian cousins. I shall have more to say about this dramatic development in the last chapter of this book. Meanwhile, there is an exciting story to tell about the time when the group as a whole was enjoying its heyday.

For convenience, students of the earth's past divide the Age of Mammals into

THE EARLIEST MAMMAL?

The fossil record is so fragmentary with respect to the early mammals that it is impossible to determine which were the "first" mammals, let alone what they looked like. They were certainly small—about rat-sized—and probably nocturnal tree-dwelling insect eaters. One such candidate is Melanodon (above), which lived in North America 160 million years ago and whose remains are among the oldest mammalian fossils ever recovered. Paleontologists suspect that it may have been an ancestor of all modern mammals.

MAMMALIAN OFFSHOOTS ON THE EVOLUTIONARY TREE

ALTICAMELUS

EPIGAULUS

Among the many bizarre-looking mammals that flourished in North America for a while and then died out were Alticamelus, a giraffelike camel of 19 million years ago, and Epigaulus, a horned rodent of 13 million years ago. Standing over 10 feet tall, Alticamelus could browse on trees. It had sharp, narrow hoofs on each of its eight toes, with flexible foot pads somewhat like those in modern camels. Epigaulus, about two feet long, was a burrower. What function its horns served is not known; the discovery of more skeletons may show that only males had them.

seven epochs. The age as a whole is known as the Cenozoic, from two Greek words, *kainos*, meaning "new," or "recent," and *zoikos*, "pertaining to life." The dating of the different epochs is determined by a variety of scientific tests applied to the rocks in which their respective fossils are embedded. The fossils themselves are the keys to the whole story. What do they tell us about the early mammals whose descendants for the past 60 million years have been such an important part of life on our planet?

To answer this question it will be easiest to consider the procession of ancient mammalian life as it appeared in the successive epochs. Some of the mammals of which fossil remains have been discovered are probably direct ancestors of mammals living today. But others, often very bizarre and intriguing, represent early mammalian forms that long ago reached the ends of their lines and died out. These fossils give us evidence of evolutionary enterprises which never came to fruition; of creatures which, through some limitation of brain power, some narrow specialization of physique or because of a sudden environmental change to which they were unable to adapt, were thrown on the scrap heap of nature's discarded experiments. The study of these ancient mammals is, however, essential to any proper understanding of the role of mammals in the world today.

The story begins in the Paleocene, which lasted from 63 million to 58 million years ago, the first epoch in the Age of Mammals. Whatever the rigors of climate which may have been a factor in the extinction of the ruling reptiles, conditions during the late Paleocene and the succeeding Eocene had become comparatively mild. The tropical and temperate zones spread out much further toward the poles than they do today. Types of plants that now flourish only in such congenial climates as that of modern Malaya were found along the banks of the Thames in England and in many of the present cold temperate zones of the United States. Even regions within the Arctic Circle supported a rich flora.

Under such attractive conditions and with no competition from the giant reptiles, the mammals began to spread over the face of the earth. By the dawn of the Eocene all the main orders of placental land mammals, including insect eaters, rodents, hoofed mammals, carnivores and early primates, were flourishing. Alongside these lived primitive monotremes and marsupials, as well as aquatic placental mammals such as whales, which had become specialized to a nonterrestrial environment by the mid-Eocene.

Among the carnivores, a group known as creodonts (literally "flesh teeth") foreshadowed the development of modern meat-eating forms. These had evolved from a line of early insect eaters which were now acquiring varying adaptations to fit them as predators on larger game. Some were rather weasel-like in shape and habit, others more closely resembled wolves and lions. One of the largest, known as hyaenodon, could kill an animal as large as a modern rhinoceros.

These early carnivorous mammals preyed on a vast assemblage of herbivorous game. Among the most spectacular herbivores was a group known as the titanotheres, or "giant beasts." Superficially resembling modern rhinoceroses, these creatures were as much as 15 feet long and eight feet high at the shoulder and had massive, bony horns on their heads. Their relatives, the chalicotheres, were odd-toed forerunners of the ungulates, or hoofed mammals, with huge birdlike claws instead of hoofs. Other Eocene mammals were the uintatheres, named after the Uinta Mountains in Utah, where their fossil remains were first found. These creatures looked formidable enough, being also as big as a modern rhinoceros and wielding tusklike upper canines and three pairs of horny protective structures on the tops of their heads. They could live only on the softest vegetable foods, however, and their mental equipment was poor—fatal limitations in the struggle for survival which soon led to their extinction.

A much more progressive line of herbivorous mammals was that of the horses, which have survived right down to modern times. A little animal known as *Hyracotherium* or eohippus (dawn horse), about the size of a fox terrier, was probably the ancestor of many later members of the group, including our familiar work horses and race horses. Instead of the characteristic hoof of modern horses, it had four toes on the front feet and three on the hind.

The elephants also trace back their pedigree to this remote epoch in the Age of Mammals. The ancestor of the modern elephant was a little swamp-dwelling creature from Egypt known as *Moeritherium*. About the size of a large pig, it had not yet developed the trunk which distinguishes its modern descendants, but had only the "blackish bulgy nose" which Rudyard Kipling described in the *Just So Stories*. *Moeritherium* was a successful little animal, nevertheless, for its trunkless snout was well adapted to cropping the vegetation along the fringes of the swamps where it made its home. Also inhabiting Egypt toward the very end of the epoch was a grotesque cousin of the elephant known as *Arsinoitherium*, with a massive tanklike body and a pair of enormous horns projecting forward above its nose.

The most dramatic water-dwelling mammal of the Eocene was an ancient whale known as *Zeuglodon*, which sometimes reached a length of between 60 and 70 feet. It was much slimmer than modern whales; in fact, its proportions remind us of descriptions of the legendary great sea serpent. Such ancestral whales were probably descendants of very early carnivorous creodonts which had abandoned evolutionary competition on dry land and explored the possibilities of the sea as a new environment for mammalian survival.

But the most potentially significant members of the mammalian cast in the Eocene were undoubtedly the primates. A wide variety of small, tree-dwelling mammals with exceptionally well-developed brains and flexible, grasping digits, they were already working out their evolutionary destiny in the treetops. They were not yet true monkeys, but were intermediate between these and their tree-dwelling insectivorous ancestors. Their fossil remains have been found in North America as well as in Europe and show that they must have been very similar to the living tarsiers and lemurs of today.

IN the next epoch, the Oligocene, which lasted from 36 million to 25 million years ago, warm conditions remained widespread and mammals continued to flourish. Eohippus evolved into a somewhat larger type of horse, known as *Mesohippus*, which stood some two feet high. It had lost the fourth toe on each front foot, an adaptation to faster running. The elephants were also increasing in size and showed the beginnings of the trunk which is so typical of their modern descendants. Some now had four tusks, two above and two below, projecting a short distance beyond the jaws, and were probably moving away from the swamps to a life on the plains. Among the contemporaries of these creatures was a group known as the anthracotheres, meaning "coal-beasts," from the coal deposits in Italy where some of their fossils were found. These were probably the animals to which the modern hippopotamuses can trace back their pedigree.

Soon after the Oligocene epoch gave place to the Miocene some 25 million years ago, the rich cast of the Age of Mammals was assembled in full splendor. The Miocene was the mammals' "golden age," a time when large-scale geological

PARACERATHERIUM

SYNDYOCERAS

The largest land mammal that ever lived, Paraceratherium was 18 feet tall and approximately 25 feet long. Its massive head alone measured four and a half feet. Dating back some 28 million years, this hornless rhinoceros, depicted here with the outline of a man to dramatize its size, lived in Asia, where it ate twigs and leaves. Syndyoceras (bottom), a deerlike inhabitant of the Nebraskan plains of 25 million years ago, stood only about three and a half feet tall at the shoulders, but the males were well armed with two sets of horns—one set curved in and the other out.

movements were buckling and twisting the earth's crust, leading to the creation of the Alpine and Himalayan chains and to a great shifting in the boundaries of land and sea. Intense volcanic activity also contributed to the changes taking place and the new mountain ranges had a profound effect on the circulation of the atmosphere. Tropical and subtropical regions were reduced and temperate conditions became more widespread. The modern world was beginning to take shape and living things began to approximate more closely the familiar types we know today.

Vast herds of herbivorous mammals thronged the Miocene plains and forests. In addition to several different kinds of horses, there were rhinoceroses, giant pigs, the first antlered deer, camels, llamas and ancestral giraffes, among many others. Elephants included a number of very oddly specialized types: one with a pair of tusks in its lower jaw which curved back toward its chest, several others with their lower jaws modified into long trough-shaped shovels which they used for digging up water plants from the floors of swamps.

PREYING on the herbivores was a varied assortment of carnivores, each adapted to hunting a different kind of quarry. These included civet cats and ancestral dogs and bears, but the most spectacular of all the carnivores were the so-called "saber-toothed tigers." Now known much more accurately as "stabbing cats," from the enormously elongated upper canines which they probably used to penetrate the thick, tough hides of young mastodons, they were a remarkably successful group throughout the Age of Mammals, but it was in the Miocene epoch that they enjoyed their heyday.

After the late Miocene, mammals in general seem to have begun a period of decline which has continued to the present day. The primates, however, continued a successful evolutionary course despite the wavering fortunes of their mammalian contemporaries. Gibbonlike apes were already swinging through the branches of the Asiatic and European forests some 20 million years ago, and the ancestors of the various kinds of Old and New World monkeys were likewise flourishing. In East Africa an exceptionally interesting great ape of that time, known as *Proconsul*, appears in the fossil record. This creature may well have been very close to the ancestry of the chimpanzee and even man.

In spite of the fact that mammals as a whole seem to have passed their peak in the late Miocene, the succeeding Pliocene and Pleistocene epochs still had a rich mammalian fauna. In the early Pliocene, giraffes were exceptionally numerous and included short-necked forms as well as the typical long-necked species we know today. A grotesque deerlike beast, *Synthetoceras*, had a huge Y-forked horn behind its nostrils, as well as conventional horns sprouting from its forehead. South America was inhabited by several giant creatures whose living cousins are today of only small or moderate size. A huge ground sloth, for instance, called *Megatherium* (literally "great beast") was as large as a modern elephant. There were also enormous armadillolike creatures known as glyptodonts (literally "sculptured tooth," from their characteristic dentition), some of which were armed with tails tipped with a cluster of vicious-looking spikes. In other parts of the world similar giant forms evolved, not only among the advanced placentals, but also among the marsupials. In Australia an extinct relation of the living wombat was as big as a rhinoceros and there were giant kangaroos between 8 and 10 feet high.

The Pleistocene epoch was periodically characterized by very rigorous conditions of climate. From about a million years ago onward, arctic conditions on

EXTINCTION AT THE HAND OF MAN

Human greed was a factor in the quick extinction of the quagga (above) and Steller's sea cow (below). South Africans ruthlessly shot the zebralike quagga in the 1860s for its handsome coat: reddish brown and white with chocolate-colored stripes on the neck. By the early 1880s the quagga no longer existed. Whaling parties butchered the defenseless Steller's sea cow for meat in such numbers that this 30-foot relative of the dugong and manatee disappeared in 1768, only 27 years after its discovery.

EXTINCTION
FROM UNKNOWN CAUSE

It is tempting to conclude that the Irish elk became extinct because evolution, "run wild," endowed it with grotesquely oversize antlers. These sometimes stretched 11 feet from tip to tip, and it has been suggested from the evidence of many skeletons in Irish bogs that the weight of the antlers mired the animals there.

Whatever doomed the elk, it was not evolution "run wild." The species disappeared in the Pleistocene, perhaps too unwieldy to escape increased pressure from wolves or early man. Predators may not have been as abundant during an earlier period when the development of large antlers could have been of temporary advantage to the elk. Later, perhaps faced with new and more numerous predators, it may have found itself out on an evolutionary limb where large antlers were no longer an advantage, but a fatal specialization.

four separate occasions imposed themselves on much of the present temperate zones. During this great ice age, vast sheets of ice advanced from the polar regions over much of the earth, driving practically all life before them. The last withdrawal started as recently as 10,000 years ago and still continues today.

The mammals of the great ice age in many cases made very effective adaptations to the harsh conditions which challenged them. Thus the Pleistocene cousins of several creatures that today have almost hairless skins were characterized by thick, shaggy coats, which helped to retain their body heat. The so-called "woolly mammoth" is a famous example of an ice age mammal that made this particular adaptation to cold. What is not so well known is that this creature also developed a thick layer of fat beneath its skin, especially on the shoulders, which probably served as a food reservoir when the frozen ground made its vegetarian diet hard to get. A woolly rhinoceros living in the same regions was protected by a similar thick covering of hair. Although hair is not normally preserved in fossil form, we know of its existence in these mammals because remains of their carcasses have survived, shaggy coat and all, in the permanently frozen ground of Siberia.

Many other species of mammals, however, were killed off in the great ice age, either through the climatic challenge of the times or by direct competition with man. This poses an interesting question: Why did some species of mammals win through while others failed? The answer lies in some of the laws controlling biological survival—and two major mammalian groups, the horses and the elephants, show in illuminating fashion how these laws work.

When the environment changes, all living things must either move to a new environment that resembles the old one or else subject themselves to the law "adapt or perish." Eohippus, the little "dawn horse," had teeth adapted only for dealing with fairly soft food, a fact which suggests that it was probably a forest dweller, living on soft shoots rather than the tough grasses of the plains. But as time went on the descendants of eohippus began to move into new environments. This occurred partly because the reduction of the forested areas of the earth led to increased competition for food and partly because of the evolution of new types of predatory carnivores with a liking for horseflesh. The descendants of eohippus thus gradually left the forests for the plains, and as a result, natural selection developed the plains horses, which were usually larger than their forest-dwelling ancestors. These gradually lost their full complement of toes and eventually supported themselves only on the center toe of each foot—the characteristic "hoof" of living horses. These larger horses could move more quickly than their tiny forebears, and their higher eye level gave them a better chance of spotting enemies on the open plains. The raising of the body on the forepart on the central toe, or hoof, gave them an exceptionally good turn of speed to outrun the plains carnivores that hunted them. Correlated with these changes came modifications in the teeth, which became adapted to grazing coarse grasses instead of nibbling the soft forest shoots. It was by such wonderful adaptations, all aimed at the single goal of survival, that the early horses became differentiated and spread across the face of the earth.

ELEPHANT evolution took a different course, but obeyed the same evolutionary principles. The early, small swamp-dwelling elephants were forced by a changing climate to develop types suited to life in drier conditions. In these new circumstances, increased size became an advantage to them, for it helped them to resist the attacks of predators in open country. Also, instead of concentrating on a speedy escape, they relied on the defensive advantages of tusks and an exceptionally thick skin. But in order to support the heavy weight of tusks, it was mechanically necessary for their necks to remain short instead of becoming elongated like those of the horses. This meant that they could not reach the ground to graze, while the tusks made browsing almost equally difficult. The answer was the development of a long prehensile upper lip, or "trunk," which could both reach the ground and extend beyond the tusks. Here again we see how, through the workings of evolution, living things may find answers to the problems of survival in a constantly changing world.

The horses and elephants were comparatively successful in their adaptations. But many other mammals, such as the great titanotheres and chalicotheres, the gigantic *Paraceratherium*, (formerly called *Baluchitherium*) and even the seemingly successful stabbing cats, have left no progeny. The hard truth of the matter, it must be re-emphasized, is that organisms must "adapt or perish," for nature does not appear to be interested in the survival of individuals, or even of different animal groups, but only in the continuation of life itself. Individuals play their part, but in themselves they are not the main object of the process.

The exceptional rigors of the ice age not only killed off many species but forced still others into extreme specializations which, in the long run, proved more disastrous than helpful. But there was another factor too: the emergence of man. Man is the most ruthless and efficient predator that evolution has yet produced. He hastened the extinction of many of the creatures of the Age of Mammals by hunting them for food and clothing. He domesticated others and harnessed them to his own use. Still others he destroyed inadvertently by drastic alterations of their environment. These processes continue today, as the spread of man's society over the face of the earth tends to eliminate more and more of the animals from whose ranks he sprang.

Whether this immense destructiveness can be justified is a question that can best be judged when, in the final chapter of this book, the role of man as a mammal has been more fully described.

ONCE COMMON IN EUROPE, AS THIS 12,000-YEAR-OLD SPANISH CAVE PAINTING SUGGESTS, BISON SURVIVE THERE TODAY ONLY IN PRESERVES

Rise and Fall of Mammals

Small creatures, the early mammals came into their own with the death of the giant reptiles. Flourishing and expanding, they evolved into a fantastic diversity of forms, a few of which are shown in the pictures on the following pages. Today they stand threatened by man, a mammal himself, who in the space of a few short years has drastically limited their numbers and variety.

The Eocene: First Flowering of the Mammals

The Eocene, 58 to 36 million years ago, was a time of great richness in mammalian development, during which many forerunners of modern animals came into being. But as this painting based on the North American fossil record shows, they still were markedly unlike the species that are familiar to us today. Eohippus, a horse ancestor that appeared in the Eocene, was no bigger than a fox terrier; *Tetonius*, one of the earliest

OPOSSUM

OXYAENA

PHENACODUS

MESONYX

TETONIUS

METACHEIROMYS

EOBASILEUS

primates, had a small skull and correspondingly small brain; *Metacheiromys*, a progenitor of the armadillo, wore a leathery shell instead of a bony one; *Hyrachyus*, a forebear of the rhinoceros, varied from wolfhound- to mustang-size. The giants of the time were the ungainly *Uintatherium* and *Eobasileus*, which stood five to seven feet tall. These, along with herbivores like *Coryphodon*, *Phenacodus* and the smaller *Palaeosyops*, were forerunners of the hoofed mammals of today. Among the flesh eaters of the Eocene whose descendants became the carnivores were the short-legged *Oxyaena*, the swift *Mesonyx* and the slender *Tritemnodon*, which may have included the opossum and the *Paramys*, a squirrel-like rodent, in its diet. Of all these mammals, the opossum is the only one that has survived, almost unchanged, into the present.

The Pleistocene: The Emergence of Modern Mammals

About a million years ago mammals over much of the world were subjected to stern evolutionary challenges by ice ages and other drastic climatic changes. This painting of an American Pleistocene landscape shows some of the types that were active during this period, although, of course, they did not all live in the same place or at exactly the same time as depicted here. Many, like the horse *Equus*, were similar to species living today.

MEGATHERIUM

DIRE WOLF

BISON

STABBING CAT

EQUUS

The Pleistocene was characterized by gigantism among many mammals. In addition to the elephant-size mastodon and woolly mammoth, there were *Megatherium*, a ground sloth measuring 20 feet in length and weighing five tons, and its smaller relative *Mylodon*. *Castoroides*, a beaver, grew to half the size of a bear, and one bison produced a 10-foot horn spread.

Size, however, was no defense against the stabbing cat. Popularly known as the "saber-toothed tiger," various forms of this animal persisted for millions of years before becoming extinct. Their long fangs were obviously used for killing but nobody is sure how. Another carnivore, the dire wolf, may have roamed in packs and brought down such hoofed animals as *Camelops*. One of the most unusual creatures of the Pleistocene was the 12-to-15-foot armored *Doedicurus*, which had a tail like a mace.

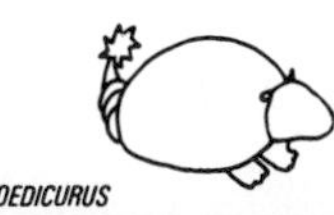

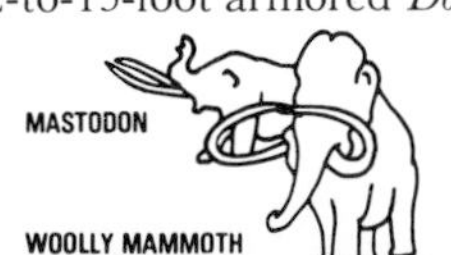

Tomorrow's Fossils

Ever since they appeared on earth around 180 million years ago, mammals, like all other living things, have evolved by adaptation to their environment and in the process the forms less well adapted have gradually died out. But perhaps never before have so many kinds of mammals disappeared in so short a time as in the last half century, during which at least 20 species have vanished; nor have so many

THE TASMANIAN WOLF, a collie-sized marsupial carnivore, survived successfully in Australia until more efficient placental mammals were introduced. It has now been nearly exterminated by men and dogs, its two greatest enemies, and is found only in remote areas of Tasmania.

THE GIANT SABLE ANTELOPE of Angola in West Africa has acute hearing and a highly developed sense of smell, which make it extremely difficult to approach. Though government protected, it is still caught in pitfalls by poachers. Only a few hundred individuals survive today.

THE BANDED ANTEATER is found today only in the extreme southwestern corner of Australia, the victim of such man-introduced animals as cats and dogs, and sheep, which destroy its habitat. This small, slow-moving marsupial is defenseless; when caught, it grunts feebly.

been threatened with extinction. It is estimated that of the approximately 4,300 species of mammals living today several hundred are in serious trouble. Some that may well become tomorrow's fossils are shown here.

Man, as the most destructive of the world's mammals, is chiefly responsible for much of this sudden dying. As he goes on cutting down forests, plowing up land and draining swamps, he so fragments and restricts the range of mammals that their populations shrink drastically. With a very small breeding stock comes the danger of matching up damaging recessive traits when the animals mate. This phenomenon, which is observable in the too-close breeding of domestic animals, tends to produce over-all genetic deterioration and ultimately hastens extinction.

THE SOLENODON, a two-foot-long nocturnal insectivore of Cuba and Haiti, has an ancient history, but its slow, waddling gait and habit of sticking its head into a hole when pursued by the dogs, cats and mongooses brought by man seem to ensure its extinction. How it got to the West Indies is difficult to say, since its nearest relatives live in Madagascar. It may be a hold-over from days when these islands were part of a continent.

THE EUROPEAN BISON, a relative of the American bison, is the largest of Europe's living mammals. Killed off by predators, disease and civilization, it ceased to exist in the wild in the early 1920s. Its continued survival in Polish, Russian and Swedish preserves and in zoos around the world depends upon selective breeding to restore genetic vigor to the stock. One hopeful sign: down to 100 after the war, the species numbers about 400 today.

Highlights of Elephant Evolution

MOERITHERIUM (EOCENE-OLIGOCENE)

PALAEOMASTODON (OLIGOCENE)

STEGODON (PLIOCENE-PLEISTOCENE)

GNATHOBELODON (PLIOCENE)

MAMMUTHUS (PLEISTOCENE)

TWO SPECIES of elephants, the Asian *Elephas maximus* and the African *Loxodonta africana*, are the last of the proboscideans, a once-numerous group of hoofed animals whose history spans 58 million years. Although it is difficult to trace in a direct line the descent of these two giants from *Moeritherium*, their earliest-known ancestor, it is possible to sketch an over-all picture of trends in the evolution of the group as a whole. This chart depicts representative proboscideans marching across geologic time. It opens with the pig-sized *Moeritherium*, which stood only two feet tall and whose heavy build, stout legs and broad, spreading feet were passed on to all members of the group. Next comes *Palaeomastodon*, the first of the mastodonts, heralding a marked tendency among proboscideans toward gigantism. It had two pairs of tusks, an upper and lower set, and the begin-

OMPHOTHERIUM (MIOCENE-PLIOCENE)

MAMMUT (MIOCENE-PLIOCENE)

PLATYBELODON (MIOCENE-PLIOCENE)

AMEBELODON (MIOCENE-PLIOCENE)

XODONTA (PLEISTOCENE-RECENT)

ELEPHAS (PLEISTOCENE-RECENT)

nings of a trunk. *Gomphotherium* was little more than a larger version of *Palaeomastodon*, but *Mammut* showed important changes—an elongated trunk, enormous upper tusks, often 8 to 10 feet in length, and a shortened lower jaw. Some proboscideans became adapted for digging roots and tubers out of the ground. *Amebelodon's* lower jaw, approximately eight feet long, had shovel-like tusks; *Platybelodon's* flared out in front to accommodate two scooplike tusks; and *Gnathobelodon's*, lacking tusks, was in the shape of a spoon and sheathed in tough skin. *Stegodon* was the first real elephant and ranged in height up to 10 feet. *Elephas* and *Loxodonta* evolved contemporaneously with *Mammuthus*, the largest of all the elephants. Unlike *Mammuthus*, which disappeared about 10,000 years ago, they continue into the present and are not yet in danger of dying out.

SWIMMING ON ITS BACK, an otter shows some of its adaptations for locomotion in the water—webbed feet, a streamlined body, a thick, sleek coat and a long, tapering tail that it can manipulate as a rudder.

3

Moving on Four Legs

IN the ability to move about from one place to another, mammals are by far the most efficient and versatile group of terrestrial vertebrates. They are not only pre-eminent on land in this respect, but have also invaded the air and reinvaded the water, where they can successfully compete with creatures who have occupied these environments for a much longer time.

The great majority of mammals may be technically classified from the point of view of locomotion as tetrapods—i.e., four-footed animals. Every order of mammals, with the exception of whales and sirenians, is mainly represented by tetrapod forms. This is a logical outcome of the evolutionary process, for the ancestors of all living terrestrial vertebrates are descended from fishes with four fins on the underside of the body, which became gradually modified for four-legged progression on land. Even the whales and sirenians were originally land-dwelling tetrapods. It was only when they reinvaded their ancestral habitat, the sea, that they lost their hind limbs, and their forelimbs became superficially finlike once more.

The movements most characteristic of land-dwelling tetrapods are walking and running. Mammals as different as the mouse, the hippopotamus, the chamois, the giraffe, the tapir, the dog and the buffalo all share the ability to walk and to run on four legs. But the story of mammalian locomotion is not altogether as simple as this. The whales and sirenians have limbs so highly specialized for aquatic life that any form of terrestrial progression, let alone walking or running, is impossible. Even among seals it is extremely difficult. Bats, on the other hand, have become specialized for life in the air. Still other mammals, the kangaroos and the little rodents known as jerboas, sometimes walk on all fours, but mainly they propel themselves on their hind limbs, using their forelimbs for other functions, such as grasping food. Several species among the primates, by contrast, progress mainly by the use of their *forelimbs*, which are much better adapted to swinging through the treetops than to making efficient movements on the ground. Finally, there is man, whose very dominance today is based partly on his ability to walk on his hind limbs alone, and thereby adapt his forelimbs for the manipulation of tools.

THE horse provides a good example of how a typical tetrapod moves. When walking, if the right forefoot is carried forward first, then the left hind foot follows. The left forefoot goes forward next, and then the right hind foot. This completes the cycle, which is immediately repeated with another advance of the right forefoot, and so on.

In the walk the center of gravity is always contained within the triangle created by three limbs placed stably on the ground. The animals can therefore stop moving at any time without falling over. Such a slow form of locomotion is not of much use, however, in the more challenging crises of life. Walking would be unlikely to bring success, for instance, to a horse attempting to evade a lion. When the tempo is quickened to a trot, each foot is lifted *before* its predecessor in the cycle has touched the ground. There is, therefore, a brief period when the animal is supported by only two of its four limbs. This makes for greater momentum but less stability.

In horses, cats, dogs and many other mammals the two limbs which are raised in this faster gait are usually diagonally opposite—the left fore and right hind foot, and vice versa. But with certain other mammals a somewhat different procedure is followed. The camel and elephant lift the limbs *on the same side*, a lateral gait known as pacing, which imparts a peculiar and quite distinctive rolling motion. This is the reason why the sensation of riding on an elephant or camel is so different from that of riding on a horse. Pacing is sometimes practiced by young or old members of species that normally adopt a

THE ADVANTAGES OF A SUPPLE SPINE

Despite its smaller size and shorter legs, a cheetah can run considerably faster than a horse, largely because of its extremely supple backbone. This can be curved like a spring, permitting the hind legs to be brought well forward on each leap to give the cheetah a very long stride. In addition, when the spine is straightened out again at the start of the next leap, added thrust is given to that already supplied by the powerful muscles of the hind legs. The disadvantage of this springlike bounding is that it consumes a great deal of energy. It is unparalleled for short sprints, but over a long course, the level-running horse will eventually outdistance the cheetah.

diagonal gait—colts, for instance, go through a pacing phase before adopting the diagonal rhythm of the adult horse.

The fastest gait characteristic of tetrapod mammals is the gallop. Here only one foot, or even no foot at all, is on the ground at certain points in the cycle. This type of movement is also well exemplified by the horse, but is practiced by such very different types of mammals as the hare and the weasel. In the gallop, the horse lifts its limbs in a different order from when it is walking, the sequence going right front, left front, right hind, left hind; or alternatively, left front, right front, left hind, right hind. At times the whole animal is flying through the air without any support whatever, and the imprints of the same hoof may be as much as 25 feet apart, some four times the length of the animal's body.

The horse's back remains comparatively rigid even at the fastest gallop, for the propulsive power is provided almost entirely by the muscles of the legs. But when such creatures as the weasel and greyhound gallop, they arch their backs at the moment of forward spring, and this greatly increases the thrust. The weasel, incidentally, shows the gallop in its simplest form. Unlike the horse, which moves its four limbs individually, it gallops in a series of bounds, moving the fore and hind limbs in pairs.

Variations between the two types of gallop practiced by the horse and the weasel also occur. The hare, for instance, bounds on paired hind feet like the weasel, but puts down its forefeet one after the other at the end of the leap.

HOWEVER they gallop, many mammals can attain quite exceptional speeds. The cheetah is the champion sprinter, overtaking its prey of swift gazelles and antelopes in half-mile bursts. French naturalist François Bourlière reports that a cheetah was clocked at 20 seconds over a distance of more than 700 yards —averaging just over 71 miles an hour, a record for mammals. Still more remarkable are its powers of acceleration, which will take it from a standing start to 45 miles per hour in two seconds—a performance that cannot be approached by even the fastest racing car. At full speed, the African wildebeest, the springbok and Thomson's and Grant's gazelles can do up to 50 miles per hour. The mighty Cape buffalo can charge at 35 miles per hour—nearly twice the average charging speed of an elephant.

Speed, of course, is very largely dependent on limb structure. Such rather slow mammals as bears and primates have feet with large, flat bearing surfaces extending from toes to heel, the whole of which are normally in contact with the ground during part of the walk. This stance is known as "plantigrade,"

derived from the Latin *planta*, meaning "the sole of the foot," and *gradior*, "to walk." The faster dog and cat, on the other hand, are "digitigrade"—they stand and walk on their "fingers," with the heel, or hock, being permanently raised. A third category of mammals, including the horses, antelopes and gazelles, is "unguligrade," progressing on the very tips of the "fingernails," which have become protected by the enlarged nails we know as hoofs.

These different structures, and their modifications, have a very strong bearing on the efficiency of their owners' movements under varying conditions. Thus the long, slender limbs of the horse are much better adapted for running swiftly over flat, but not slippery, surfaces than the shorter limbs of the flat-footed bears. Conversely, on ice a bear will do much better, for its broad sole gives it a much better frictional grip and it will not, like the horse, be in constant danger of falling.

The sure-footed mountain sheep and goats have feet that are especially adapted for travel in rugged mountainous terrain. Their hoofs have sharp edges and the undersides are concave, enabling them to adhere somewhat like suction cups as these agile creatures make their way up and down seemingly impassable cliffs. Caribou have huge rounded hoofs to support their weight on snow or spongy tundra, and the edges of the hoofs are sharp to prevent skidding on ice. The camel's cloven hoofs are very broad and cushioned with thick soles—adaptations for travel over yielding desert ground. But Bactrian camels are animals of cold climates, which suggests that this hoof structure may have originally been an adaptation to snow. A number of arctic mammals as different as the polar bear, the Canada lynx and the snowshoe hare have broad, flat feet with furred soles that act as snowshoes.

THE TROT AND THE PACE

Trotting and pacing are economical gaits that allow animals to maintain speed over long distances. In the trot, alternate legs move together, i.e., left front and right rear, as shown by the horse above. In the pace, the two legs on the same side move together, here demonstrated by a camel. This shifts the animal's weight from side to side as it moves, making the camel less comfortable to ride.

MAN, by nature a plantigrade primate, is unique among mammals in the extreme specializations he has made to a bipedal stance, but there are several members of other mammalian orders which have tended in this direction. The locomotion of such creatures is particularly well illustrated by the kangaroos and the jerboas. A typical large kangaroo, such as the great red kangaroo of Australia, has one of the oddest gaits in the animal kingdom. When moving slowly it uses not four supporters but five, for the thick muscular tail functions as a fifth supporting limb. With all four feet as well as its tail on the ground, the kangaroo raises its two hind limbs together, its body weight carried by the short forelimbs and the tail; as part of the same movement the hind limbs swing forward to a new position. The forelimbs are then likewise raised and moved forward, and the cycle repeats itself.

As the pace quickens, however, kangaroos adopt a quite different action—the familiar leaping gait for which they are famous. In this, only the hind limbs come into contact with the ground, which they do simultaneously and side by side. The body is carried well forward and is counterbalanced by the tail, which stretches out behind. The exceptionally long and powerful hind legs propel the animal forward in a series of jumps, which can be maintained at a steady pace of upwards of 20 miles per hour. In short bursts a speed of about 30 miles per hour can be achieved. The leaps themselves are normally some five times as long as the kangaroo's body length—that is to say, some 25 feet—but leaps of 40 feet have been recorded. From a standing start the maximum height of a kangaroo's jump is about eight feet.

The Old World jerboas and the New World kangaroo rats and jumping mice move very much like miniature kangaroos. Their hind limbs are even longer in proportion to their forelimbs than are those of kangaroos, and their tails are likewise used for balance.

Such gaits as walking, running and leaping are practiced mainly by mammals that habitually live on the ground. A few mammals, such as moles and pocket gophers, spend practically their entire lives underground. Both have short, powerful forelimbs equipped with strong claws for digging, and moles have their entire forelimbs broadened and flattened into efficient shovels.

A MUCH larger number of mammals have wholly or partly abandoned life on the stable earth for a new kind of existence in the leafy world of the treetops. In this comparatively unstable environment, the tail is mostly used as a balancing organ, but in some tree dwellers it has become modified to the point where it actually functions as a fifth grasping limb—a most useful adaptation. Many different mammals have tails that are more or less prehensile: the African long-tailed pangolin, the binturong of southeast Asia and the Papuan arboreal mouse, for instance. South America has numerous examples, among them monkeys, opossums, the tree porcupine, the silky anteater and the kinkajou. Such South American primates as the spider monkeys, woolly monkeys and howlers have such powerful prehensile tails that they can support the whole of their body weight by this organ alone.

Another even more important adaptation to movement in the trees is in the structure of the limbs themselves. There is a tendency, particularly noticeable in the arboreal primates, for the hind limbs to become stronger and heavier than the forelimbs. This is because the hind limbs are generally used for supporting the body weight while the forelimbs reach about in search of new holds. This tendency has had an extremely important effect on the evolution of man.

A number of characteristic modifications also occur in the digits of many tree-dwelling mammals. These are usually long and flexible and are well suited to grasping the branches through which the animals move. But a special advantage is provided by the thumb, which to a greater or lesser extent is separated from the other digits and can be opposed to them to grasp objects or to complete the encirclement of the limb of the tree. This opposable thumb, found in various stages of development in opossums and primates as well as other mammals, has reached a particularly high state of refinement in man—a fact that confirms other evidence of our descent from tree-dwelling ancestors.

As we move down the scale from the primates to less advanced mammals we find that the adaptations of the limbs to arboreal life are simpler, though these may still be very effective. Nails or claws are developed to varying degrees as aids to clinging to branches or bark. One very specialized adaptation is found in the tarsier, which in addition to flexible digits has expanded pads on the toes with cross striations which offer an exceptionally high degree of frictional resistance. They operate, in fact, on the same principle as the tread of a tire or a ridged rubber mat.

Various methods of climbing vertical tree trunks are used by different mammals. Monkeys usually ascend by grasping first with one hand and then with the diagonal, or opposite, foot. Squirrels may gallop up the trunk, taking alternate holds with their front and hind limbs. Bears hug the trunk with their forelimbs, taking successive holds with the sharp, curved claws of all four feet. The slow and deliberate Canadian porcupine is helped in its climbing by granular nonskid pads on the soles of its feet, as well as by modified spines growing at the base of the underside of the tail—a climbing aid found in similar form in the African spiny-tailed squirrel. When descending trees, most mammals come down tail first, but squirrels usually scuttle down headfirst, as does the fisher.

In certain primates, movement through the trees is achieved by the arm-swinging process known as brachiation. This is a kind of inversion of the bipedal walk, in which the forelimbs instead of the hind limbs are used alternately to carry the body along. Gibbons and spider monkeys, with exceptionally long forelimbs and hooklike hands, are typical brachiators. The long limbs increase the momentum with which the animal can project itself forward. The fingers and the palm of the hand are exceptionally elongated, giving a greater surface for contacting a bough after a leap. A marked curvature of the bones of the hand still further increases its likeness to a hook or grapple. The thumb is correspondingly reduced so as not to impede rapid release in swinging from bough to bough, and the muscles which flex the digits are shortened so that the hand in a position of rest is curled inward. Swinging along hand over hand through the trees at great speed, gibbons often throw themselves 20 feet or more through the air between alternate holds.

SEVERAL groups of arboreal mammals are accomplished gliders. The North American flying squirrels are beautiful little nocturnal beasts which have membranes of fur-covered skin connecting the wrists of the forefeet and the ankles of the hind feet. Leaping outward into space, they spread their limbs and gliding membranes, and sail—sometimes 150 feet or more—to another and lower landing place. The Australian sugar gliders, which resemble the North American flying squirrels in appearance, glide in the same way. The flying lemurs of the Malay archipelago and the Philippines have similar gliding membranes between the neck, the limbs and the tail, but they extend through the fingers, giving them a webbed appearance.

The mammals which have achieved true flight are represented solely by the bats, whose greatly elongated forelimbs and fingers serve as supports, or struts, for the thin membranes forming the flying surfaces of their wings. Except for the short, clawed thumbs, which are free for grasping, the elongated fingers are all enclosed by these membranes. Extending back along the sides, the membranes are usually attached to the hind limbs at the ankles. The hind toes are free and are used for holding on when the bat rests in its typical upside-down attitude. Another membrane stretches between the two hind limbs, usually enclosing most of the tail. This tail membrane also acts as a net in which insect food can be scooped up.

This wing structure is quite different from that found in birds, in which the flight feathers are supported by the bones of the "forearm." In spite of their different wing structure, however, the actual movements of bats in flight are closely comparable to those of birds. In both, the wing is moved downward and forward in one motion, and then backward and upward in another. Both bats and birds can also glide, although bats largely lack the ability to soar on wind currents or rising currents of warm air with the typical grace and economy of movement which many birds achieve. A few bats can also hover, but not with the seemingly effortless ease of the hummingbirds. The style of flying varies greatly with different species of bats. The majority have an uneven, fluttering flight, which is well described in their German name of *Fledermaus*, or "flitter mouse." Others—for example, the tropical Molossidae, which have long, narrow wings—can achieve a faster, somewhat more even flight resembling that of swifts. The largest living bats, the so-called flying foxes of Malaya, may have a wing span of between four and five feet and are capable of sustaining powerful flight for long periods.

When not airborne in search of insects and other food, bats usually hang upside down by their hind legs in dark places such as hollow trees and caves. They do most of their flying at night, and zoologists were long intrigued by the mystery of how they avoided obstacles in total darkness. Then some years ago, two American scientists, Donald R. Griffin and Robert Galambos, applying modern techniques to the 18th Century experiments of the Italian Lazzaro Spallanzani and the Swiss Charles Jurine, conducted some ingenious research at Harvard University to find out just how bats did this. Blinding the bats by sealing their eyes shut had no effect, for the bats avoided obstacles as skillfully as ever. But if their ears were plugged or their jaws tied shut and their mouths sealed, the bats blundered into wires. Other senses than sight were obviously being used. Hearing had something to do with it, and so did the bat's voice. Research eventually showed that the typical abilities of bats in the dark depend on a system of echo location.

What happens is this. Bats, when not actually asleep, give out a number of sounds, varying from an audible click to a cry so shrill that it cannot be heard by the human ear, although it can be detected by instruments. Even when the animal is stationary before taking flight, some half dozen or more of these ultrasonic cries may be given out every second. In normal flight the rate is stepped up to about 20 or 30 a second; when some obstacle is approached it is increased still more. The sound waves of these ultrasonic cries bounce off solid objects and the echoes travel back to the bat's ears, thus keeping the bat informed of the presence and distance of the obstacles. How the bat discriminates between various types of echoes—for instance, between an obstacle to be avoided and an insect to be caught—we do not yet know. This particular adaptation to a highly specialized way of living, now often termed "bat sonar," is one of the most fascinating and beautiful to be found in nature.

FINALLY we come to the swimming mammals, which represent another extreme form of adaptation to a special environment. *All* land-dwelling vertebrates probably developed originally from aquatic ancestors, the lobe-finned fishes; and mammals themselves are the end product of an evolutionary line which had passed through an earlier amphibian and reptilian phase. Between 50 and 60 million years ago, however, certain mammals reinvaded the water, the once-familiar environment of their remote ancestors. The range of adaptations they made to aquatic life is considerable, and the creatures possessing them can be divided for purposes of simple description into three main groups.

First there are those mammals which, although normally land dwellers, can take to the water quite successfully in special circumstances. Thus, unlikely as it may seem, such creatures as hares, hedgehogs, mice, moles, weasels, cats and even elephants are excellent swimmers if the need arises. The efficiency of these animals in water, however, is really based on their capacity to use physical equipment primarily designed for land life. To take only one amusing example, swimming hamsters inflate their cheek pouches as an aid to buoyancy.

In the second group we can list a number of mammals with structures which are primarily adapted for aquatic use. The webbed feet of such mammals as the otter and the platypus, and the rudderlike tail of the beaver are obviously designed especially for aquatic locomotion. The otter swims mainly by fishlike undulations of the body, but the comparatively broad surface of the webbed toes, which offers much greater resistance to the water than would individual digits, imparts an additional thrust and also allows the animal to make exceptionally rapid twists and turns. In the platypus, the webs of the front feet extend some distance beyond the toes, giving more thrusting surface in the water. The yapock, or water opossum, of tropical America uses its webbed hind feet while pursuing fish and other prey in streams. It is the only aquatic marsupial. An aquatic insectivore, the Himalayan water shrew has stiff hairs growing between its toes which serve the same function as webs. The beaver, which uses its horizontally flattened, blade-shaped tail for both sculling and steering in the water, shows how swimming ability can be achieved with an entirely different anatomical device. The muskrat uses its vertically compressed tail in much the same way.

THE third group contains the most highly specialized water-dwelling mammals of all: the seals and their allies, the sirenians, or sea cows, and the whales and dolphins. Although their ancestors were four-footed land mammals, these creatures have long since become so efficiently adapted to water-dwelling life that many of them have entirely lost the ability to move about on land. The earless seals and the walrus may use all four webbed feet while swimming, although seals often propel themselves—sometimes belly up—with their hind limbs alone. The sea elephants also swim with their hind limbs and usually keep their front flippers pressed to their sides. But eared seals such as the Alaskan fur seal and the California sea lion propel themselves principally with their forelimbs, while the hind limbs are employed for steering.

The sea cows are so adapted to a watery existence that they have lost their hind limbs entirely, retaining only their paddle-shaped front limbs. Somewhat resembling the legendary mermaid in general shape (but not in appearance), sea cows have often been regarded as the source of the majority of mermaid "sightings" described by credulous voyagers through the centuries. One close-up look at a sea cow's wrinkled face and bristling cheeks, however, would change the mind of any believer. The largest of the sea cows, Steller's sea cow of North Pacific waters, measured from 25 to 30 feet long and weighed about three and a half tons. It was completely exterminated in the mid-18th Century by the depredations of fur hunters who slaughtered these harmless animals for food. The living sea cows, known as the manatee and the dugong, have also been much reduced in numbers by excessive hunting, even though they are now strictly protected in many areas.

Whales and dolphins represent a still more extreme stage of specialization. In fact, they have reacquired so many structures characteristic of their aquatic ancestors, such as fins, fluked tails and torpedo-shaped bodies, that they are still often mistaken for fish. The fin of a whale, however, differs as much in structure from the fin of a fish as the wing of a bat from the wing of a bird. As with sea cows, the hind limbs have been lost, though many species still have vestigial hind-limb bones buried deep in their flesh. Whales propel themselves with powerful up and down strokes of their tails, which have two flukes and, unlike the vertical tails of fishes, are flattened in a horizontal plane. The fins are used mainly for steering.

These are just a few of the varied structures that mammals have acquired as an aid to efficient movement in their different environments. Beautifully adapted to the functions they are called upon to fulfill, they form a vitally important part of each animal's equipment in the constant struggle for survival.

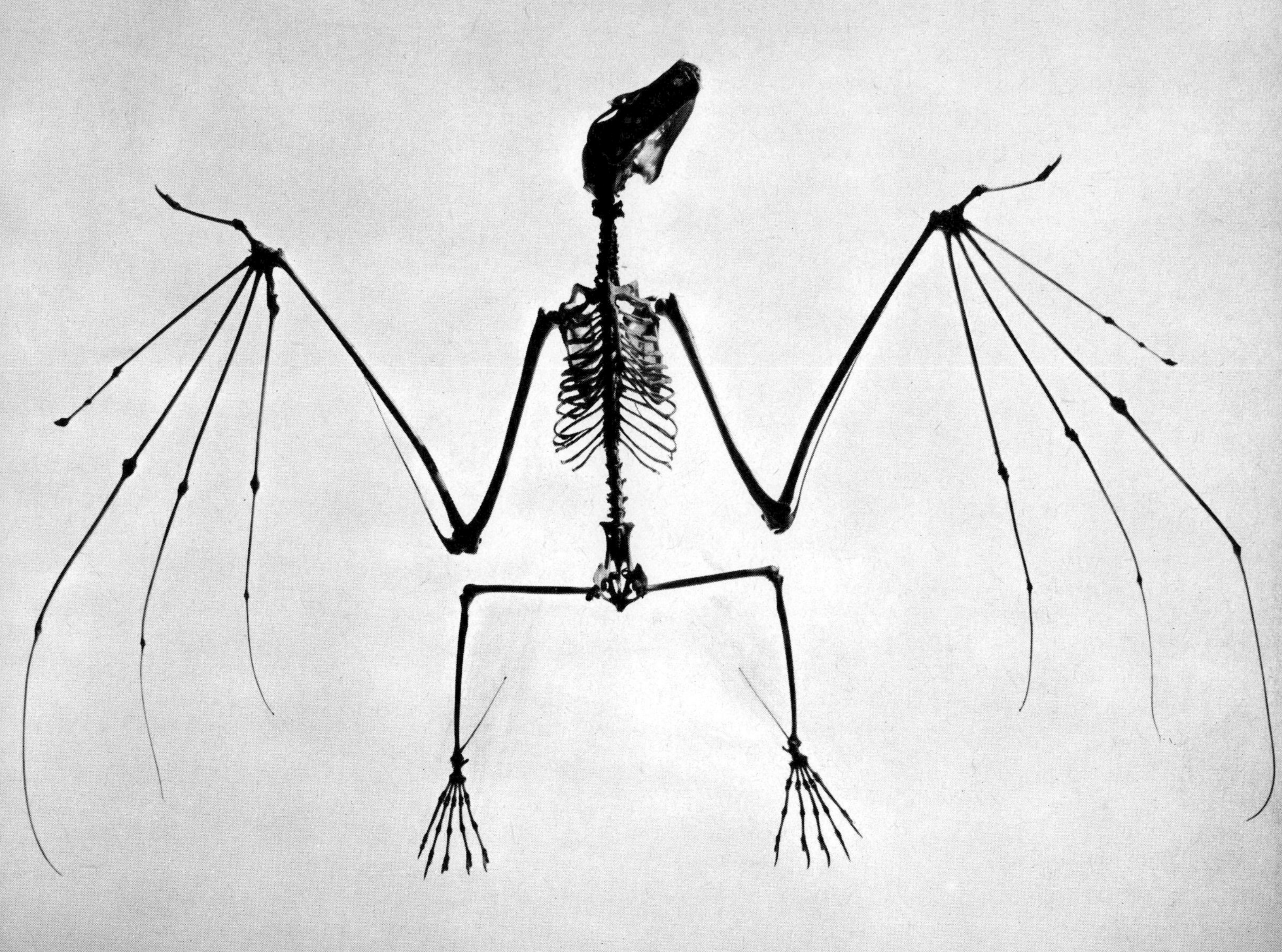

A FRUIT-BAT SKELETON REVEALS THE GREATLY ELONGATED FINGERS DEVELOPED BY BATS FOR THE SUPPORT OF THEIR MEMBRANOUS WINGS

Mammalian Locomotion

The marked ability of mammals to move quickly and strongly is one of their outstanding characteristics. Generally more agile than the reptiles from which they are descended, and possessed of considerably more endurance, the mammals have developed a bewildering diversity of limbs, feet and toes, which enable them to get about effectively in the great variety of environments they inhabit.

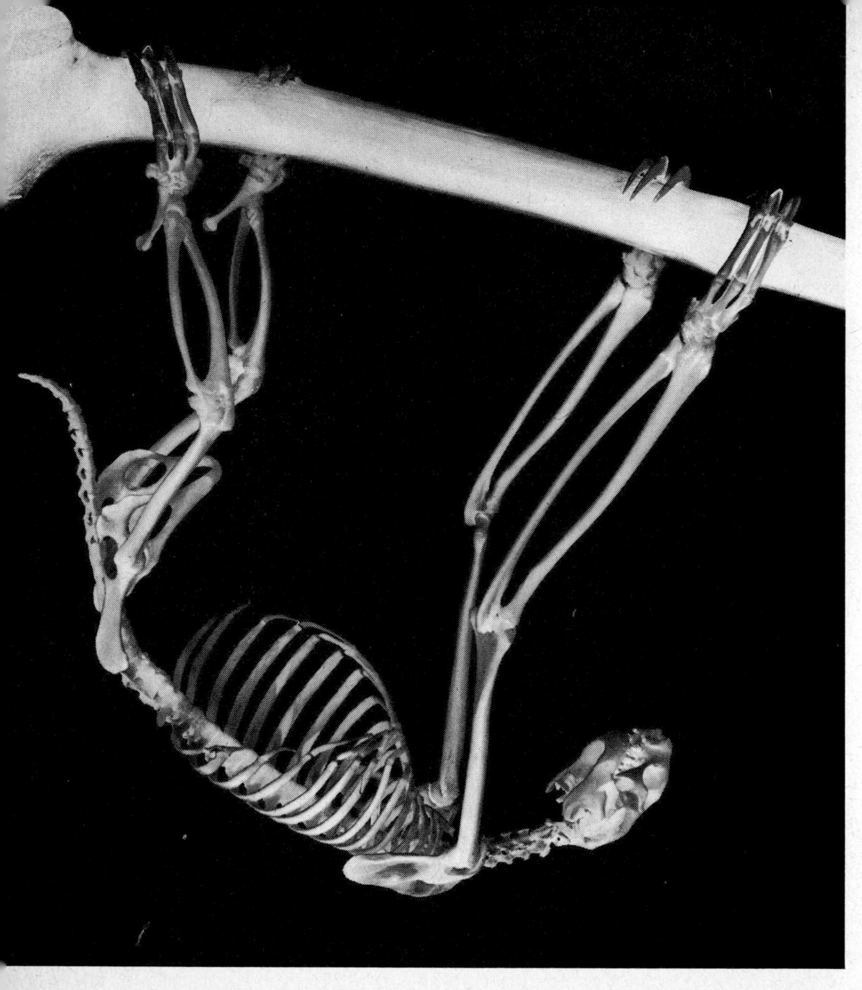

Adaptation of the Skeleton

The different ways by which different mammals move about have been determined largely by their ability to respond to the evolutionary challenges of getting food and escaping their enemies. Some of the fastest-running mammals have evolved in a flat, dry habitat where feeding must be done over wide areas and out in the open. Among the slowest are the sloths *(left)*, which have for their habitat trees of the American tropics, where they eat the foliage. They have developed extremely long forelimbs for moving upside down along branches, but are almost helpless on the ground. Among the greatest leapers for their size are the jerboas and kangaroo rats. Jumping about

ELONGATED FORELIMBS and shorter hind legs of the three-toed sloth end in curved claws that hook over branches. Sloths often sleep in this position.

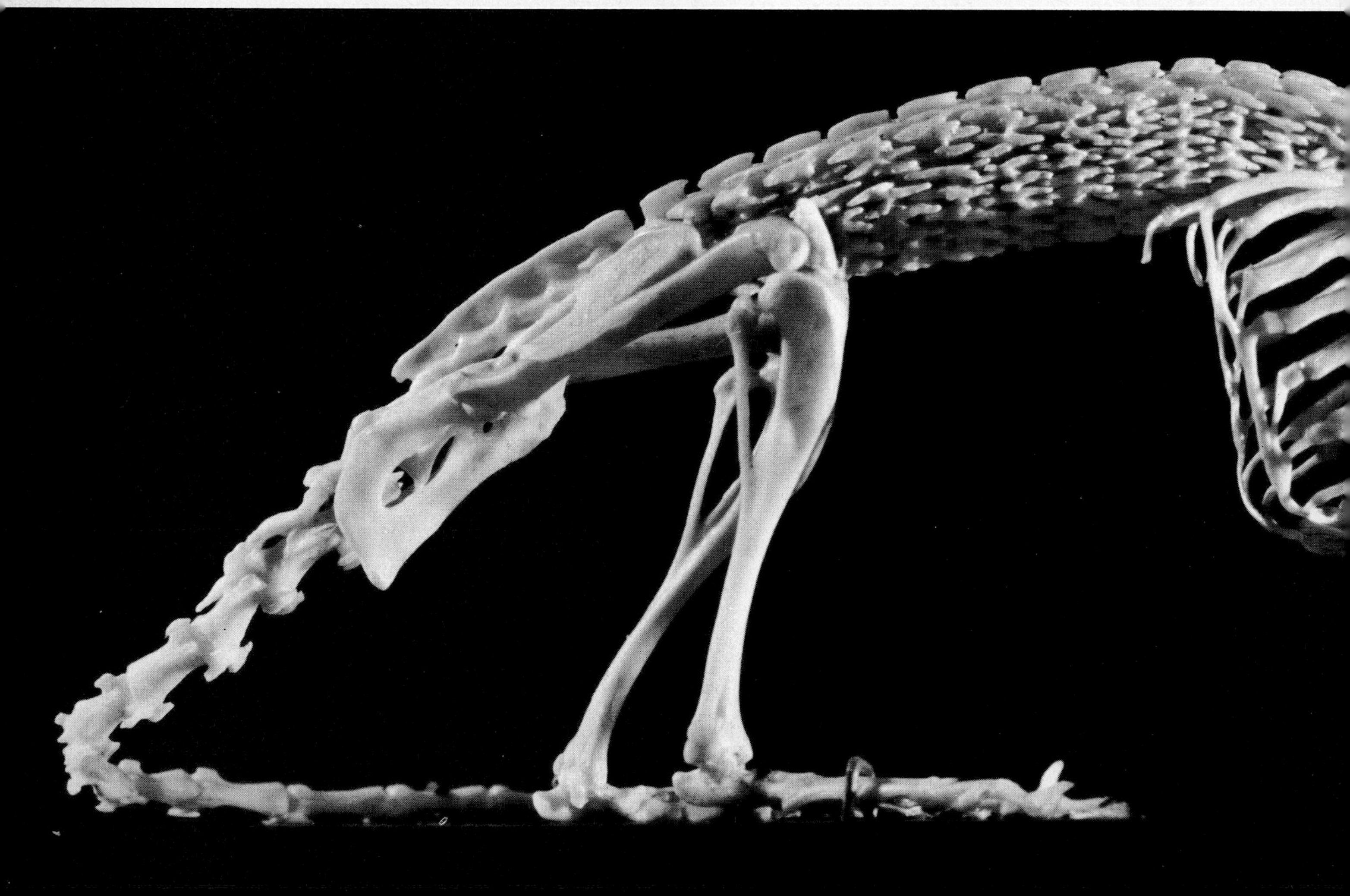

UNUSUALLY CONSTRUCTED SPINE OF THE AFRICAN HERO SHREW CAN SUPPORT THE WEIGHT OF A 160-POUND MAN. MADE OF INTERLOCKING VERTEBRAE

in search of food, they would be vulnerable targets were it not for their ability to dodge predators by leaping away from them. Their specializations for a bipedal mode of locomotion include enormously long hind legs, a long tail for balance and a chunky body which is easy to catapult.

Though different, the skeletons of the sloth and jerboa, like those of all other placental mammals, may derive from those of small ancient insectivores that scampered around on all fours. These archaic skeletons are believed to have been not unlike that of the hero shrew's below, which, despite its unusual backbone, retains many primitive features still found among the insectivorous shrews.

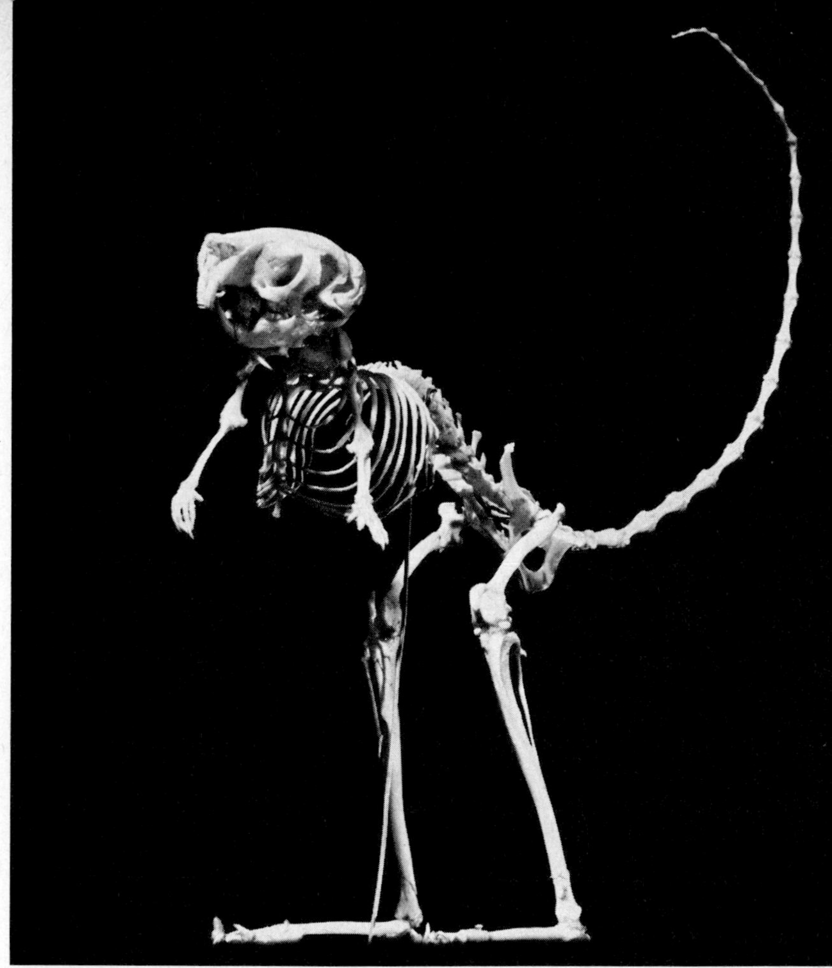

EXAGGERATED HIND LEGS of a jerboa give tremendous leverage, enabling it to jump six feet or more, although its body is only six inches long.

AND ARCHED FOR ADDED STRENGTH, IT MAY ENABLE THE SHREW TO HUNT FOR INSECTS UNDER PILES OF LOOSE ROCKS WITHOUT BEING CRUSHED

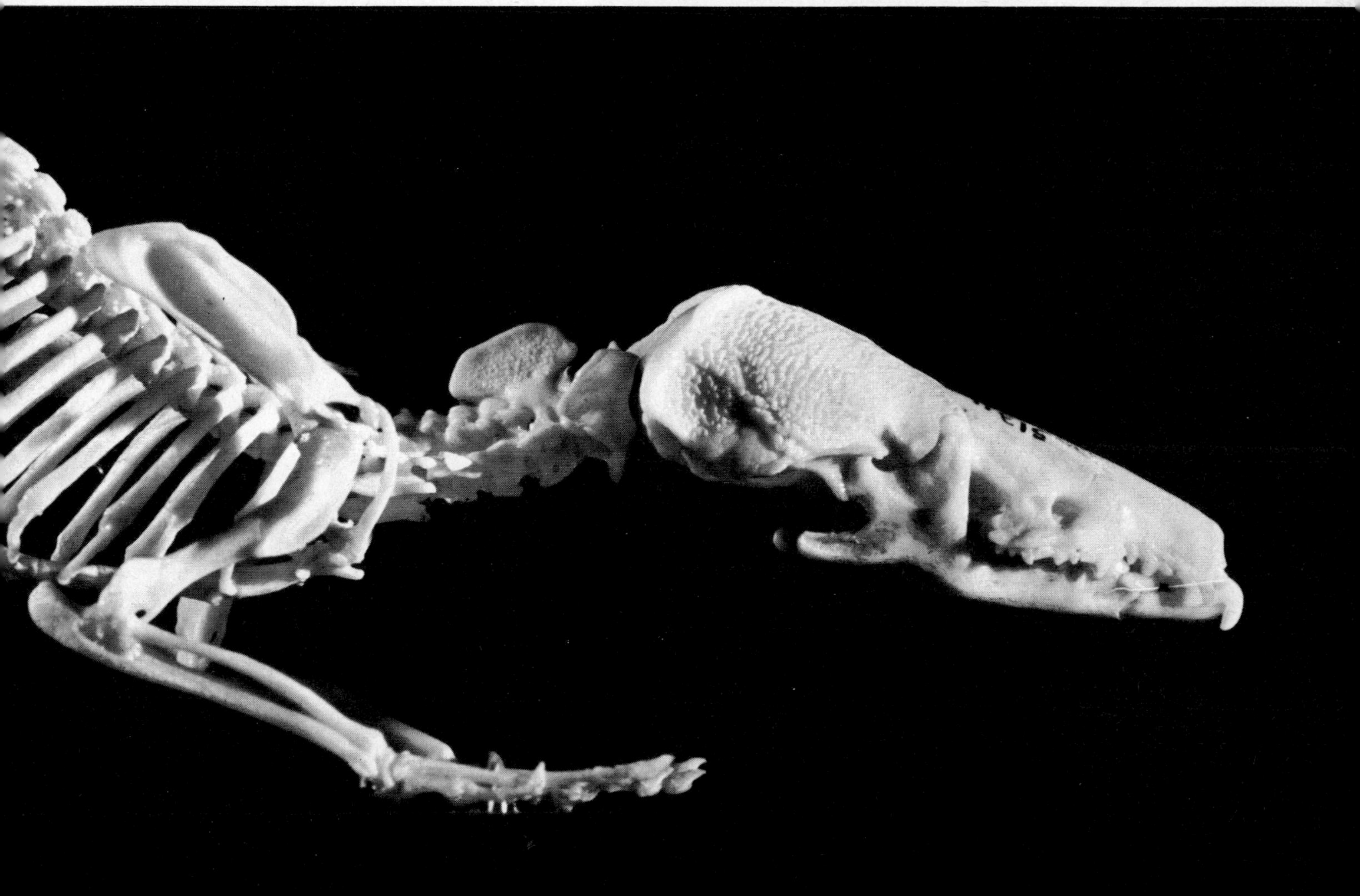

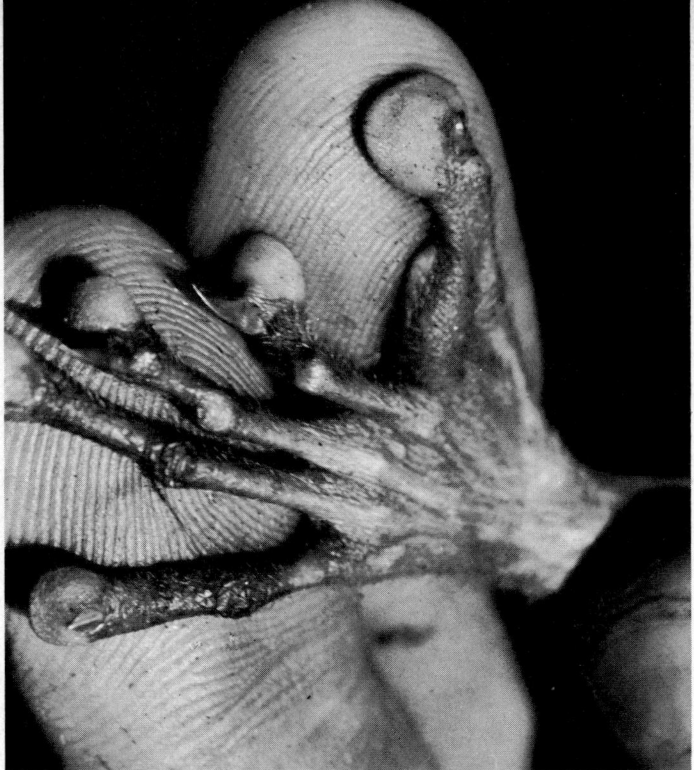

BULBOUS FINGER TIPS of a tarsier provide greater skin surface and improve this nocturnal primate's ability to cling to objects. The fingers and toes are also ridged on their bottoms to increase friction.

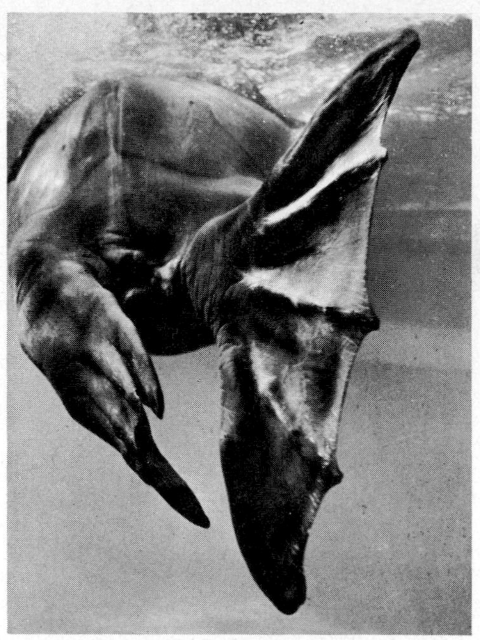

PADDLELIKE REAR FLIPPER of a walrus opens wide to provide propulsive power. On the return stroke, it will fold like the other flipper.

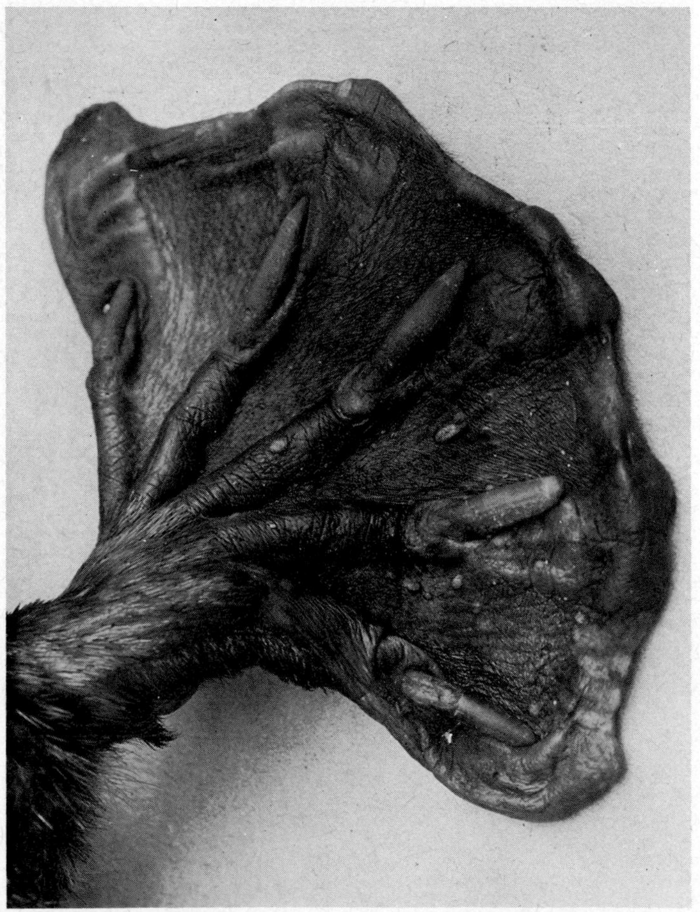

OVERSIZE WEBBING of an Australian platypus's forefoot is shown extended, as it would be if the animal were swimming. It can be tucked under the paw to free the claws for the excavation of a burrow.

Feet—and Their Many Uses

The foot shape of a mammal says a good deal about how its owner gets its food. The tree-dwelling tarsier leaps after insects and lizards and possesses hands and feet which provide a maximum of friction surface for a secure grip on branches. The platypus is a water-dwelling animal with a ravenous appetite. It paddles with its forefeet, searching the muddy bottoms of creeks and rivers for the hundreds of shrimps, tadpoles, worms, crayfish and larvae it can consume in a night. Its forefeet, one of which is seen at left, are generously webbed, and the swimming membrane even extends beyond the claws to make a large, efficient paddle. Moles, another group of active animals, also have specialized forefeet *(opposite)* with which they burrow after worms, insects and larvae. The walrus, though lacking feet in the strict sense of the word, has flippers, which are the modified limbs of its terrestrial ancestors. Feeding on shellfish in arctic and subarctic seas, it need not be a swift swimmer like some of the fish-pursuing seals, but must be a powerful diver, and its heavy frame and large rear flippers *(above)* help it to be one.

STOUT PAWS enable a mole to dig long tunnels in the ground. Clawing into the hard soil, the mole pushes the broken pieces under its body and kicks them to the rear with its hind legs. It can tunnel 12 to 15 feet an hour. It rolls over slowly on its head to turn itself around and bulldozes the accumulated loose soil into a pile—the molehill—at the entrance of its burrow.

JUMPING A FENCE, a kangaroo shows the form that enables individuals weighing 200 pounds to leap as far as 27 feet. Kangaroos reach top speeds of about 30 miles an hour.

Mammals in High Gear

Many of the fastest mammals are found among the large herbivores, and it is easy to understand why: they must be able to run from the large carnivores. The galloping giraffes shown on the opposite page and the impala below display several specializations of the hoofed animals for speed—long legs for a long stride, light shank muscles for quick action and heavy thigh muscles for power. The kangaroo, by contrast, has only one pair of long legs, and these are well muscled throughout to thrust its heavy body from the ground. On its high-flying leaps, it uses its long, thick tail as a counterbalance and rudder.

SPRINGING THROUGH BRUSH, an African impala stretches its body into a graceful arc. The impala is capable of making explosive leaps 8 feet high and 25 feet long.

TAKING ENORMOUS STRIDES, giraffes gallop at the rate of 28 to 32 miles an hour, but the slow rhythm of their long, heavy legs makes them appear to be doing less.

WITH LEGS SPREAD TO UNFURL FOLDS OF SKIN ALONG ITS SIDES, A FLYING SQUIRREL GLIDES IN FOR A LANDING CLOSE TO ITS DEN IN A DEAD TREE.

Getting About in the Trees

In exploiting the trees as a source of food and shelter, the arboreal mammals have developed various techniques for moving from branch to branch and tree to tree which minimize their contacts with the ground. The nocturnal flying squirrel *(above)*, an elusive but fairly common inhabitant of most North American forests, is an adept glider. Leaping from a branch, it spreads its legs to stretch the loose folds of skin running from wrist to ankle on either side of its body. It can sail downward on these folds at an angle of about 40 or 50 degrees for distances of 150 feet—or more, if the ground below slopes. It can

DRAGGING ITSELF FORWARD WITH ITS CLAWS, A TWO-TOED SLOTH MANAGES TO REACH A TREE. IT CLIMBS TO A BRANCH AND PROGRESSES UPSIDE

BY WHISKING ITS TAIL UPWARD, IT RIGHTS ITSELF, AND THE BILLOWING SKIN FOLDS CHECK ITS SPEED. ALIGHTING IT SCRAMBLES INTO THE DEN

even direct its course by raising, lowering or extending its legs, and balancing with its tail.

The sloth *(below)*, lacking the flying squirrel's agility and swiftness, is nevertheless well adapted to its jungle habitat. A highly specialized animal, it depends almost exclusively on the leaves of one type of tree for its food and on unobtrusiveness for its protection. It forages by inching along a branch in an upside-down position, using its claws as grappling hooks. Thus suspended, it is difficult to attack—and even more difficult to see, for green algae growing in its fur make it blend with the background.

DOWN ALONG THE BRANCH AT THE RATE OF ABOUT A THIRD OF A MILE AN HOUR. SLOTHS SPEND THE GREATER PART OF A DAY DOZING AND SLEEPING

0 MPH
10 MPH
20 MPH
30 MPH
40 MPH

The Top Speeds of Animals

IF MAMMALS were pitted against insects, fishes, reptiles and birds in a race, they would fare like this: The cheetah, running at a top speed of 70 miles an hour, would be out in front, outdistanced only by the golden eagle, Indian swift and peregrine falcon. But having less staying power, the cheetah would eventually be overtaken by the Mongolian gazelle, whose short body and long legs give it great endurance on long runs.

Across the top of the painting is a scale of speeds in miles per hour. Man is shown in sprints—the 100-yard dash and the 100-yard swim. The race horse is mounted because a horse will run faster if goaded by a rider.

DAINTILY DISSECTING a dandelion, a prairie dog gets ready for a meal. These burrowing rodents are voracious competitors of grass-feeding livestock, but they also may take advantage of grasshopper swarms to augment their vegetarian diets.

4

How Mammals Eat

FOOD is the fuel which makes the body machine work, and without it living things quickly lose their energy and eventually die. Plants do not "eat" in the sense that we usually understand that term, but they do synthesize organic food, using chemicals in the soil and the air as ingredients, and the rays of the sun as the source of energy. The lowest animals, on the other hand, absorb their nourishment directly through their body coverings. Thus the amoeba, although lacking a mouth, surrounds food particles and absorbs them through the flexible membrane in which it is enclosed.

In the higher animals this process of taking in food has become much more complex. To get their essential nourishing fuel and to break it down for energy, mammals, like other vertebrates, have to perform a whole series of complicated operations. First, of course, each animal has to find an actual supply of the kind of food suited to its particular bodily needs. A cat will starve if only grass is available, whereas a horse will be able to subsist on it for an indefinite period.

Second, the animal must actually get the food into its mouth. This is not nearly so simple an operation as one might think. Even with vegetarian species many problems arise. For example, the long-necked giraffe, whose head can reach the ground only after a laborious straddling of the legs, would find it impossible to survive unless it lived in the vicinity of bushes and trees that brought its food within easy reach. Conversely, a short-necked grass eater suddenly transferred to a forest environment would be in equally dire straits. The tree cover would make it impossible for grass to grow on the forest floor, and the animal's lack of height would prevent it from reaching the foliage above even if its teeth and digestion were capable of dealing efficiently with a new diet of leaves and shoots. With meat eaters the problem is even greater. Not only must suitable prey be available, but the animal must actually capture it, either by running it down, by lying in wait and ambushing it, or by some other hunting technique.

But finding food and getting it to the mouth are still only the beginning of the problem. A further complex sequence of events must occur before the food can perform its function of nourishing the animal and keeping it alive. First the mouth itself must be equipped with suitable machinery for dealing with the particular food it receives. In most mammals this machinery is provided by the teeth, and these vary enormously from species to species in arrangement and structure. In general, mammals have four different kinds of teeth—incisors, canines, premolars and molars. The incisors, at the front of the jaws, are normally designed for nipping, cutting and gnawing; the canines, which lie next to them, for seizing and tearing; and the premolars and molars, at the back of the jaws, for grinding and chewing. All these teeth may be enormously modified, however, to fit the animal for particular diets or to deal with the other biological pressures which may affect its survival.

In some mammals the modifications of the teeth have gone so far that some of the teeth are no longer used for biting or chewing at all, but are adapted to perform quite different functions. The tusks of the elephant are highly modified incisors, but they play no part in mastication. Instead they are used for attack and defense, and for rooting food from the ground or breaking branches from trees.

WHEN a mammal swallows food, usually after chewing it, the food passes into the esophagus, a simple passage which conveys it quickly to the much wider envelope known as the stomach. Here the proteins are broken down by the action of the gastric juices, and the food goes on to the small intestine. Now reduced to a sort of mush, it continues to break down into simpler components, some of which are immediately absorbed into the blood stream. These processes continue in the caecum and large intestine, nourishing matter being absorbed in different proportions into the blood stream as the journey proceeds. Finally, the unused residue is passed out through the rectum and returned to the soil as manure to enrich the food supply on which future generations may feed.

Although the basic biological mechanism for assimilating food is much the same in all mammals, there are enormous differences in the diets of different species. Broadly speaking, mammals may be classified in terms of their food intake into three groups: the strictly vegetarian forms; the strictly carnivorous forms; and the so-called omnivorous forms, which take both vegetable and animal nourishment. But the division is not really so simple as it appears, for the feeding habits of mammals may be modified by many factors. Hunger is a great spur to adaptability, and a food which in congenial circumstances would be ignored might in more challenging conditions be pounced on. The diet will also vary considerably with the seasons, with the age of the animal and with the state of its health. Few mammals are so specialized for one form of diet that they cannot, in an emergency, make do for a time on food that they would not normally accept.

It is often hard to determine exactly what a mammal's diet is. Everyone knows that lions normally eat meat and that cows eat grass. But with small nocturnal mammals, which are very difficult to study by direct observation, the scientist has to fall back on other techniques, such as investigations of the stomach contents of dead specimens or analysis of the animal's droppings. These techniques can give a fairly accurate picture of the mammal's feeding habits although it may never be observed eating at all.

By far the greatest number of mammals are vegetarians. They eat different vegetable foods according to the particular adaptations of their anatomy, especially their teeth, and the availability of these foods in the regions they inhabit. Grasses, shoots and leaves are basic foods utilized by many vegetarian mammals, but these by no means exhaust the list. Certain species show most interesting adaptations to more specialized diets.

The inhabitants of exceptionally dry regions provide a remarkable example of this. For instance, the Egyptian gerbil and the kangaroo rats and pocket mice of the southwestern deserts of the United States can subsist quite happily on seeds which have a water content of less than 10 per cent. Even when given nothing to drink, these animals will prosper and fatten, whereas a brown rat in similar conditions will quickly become dehydrated and die. Obviously the physiology of these desert species is exceptionally well adapted to conserve water necessary to maintain their vital processes.

Among other vegetarian foods enjoyed by mammals are nectar, fruits, bark, fungi and nuts. Certain tropical bats subsist on a diet of nectar drawn from night-blooming flowers. Various other bats—and some monkeys—live almost exclusively on fruits and cannot survive unless the fruits they are accustomed to are available. The range of the moustached white-nosed monkey of west Central Africa, for example, appears to be controlled by the presence of palm trees of the genus *Elaeis*, which produce the fruits which form its staple food.

Bark would not seem to offer many gastronomic rewards, but it is nevertheless a favorite food with many mammals. The North American moose consumes it in large quantities, and the bark of willows, poplars and aspens forms the main winter food supply of the beavers of the same region. The North American porcupine subsists largely on the inner bark of conifers and hardwoods, its incisor teeth being well adapted for stripping it from the trees. In winter, when other food is scarce, voles and rabbits often live on bark stripped from the lower trunks and branches of young trees. The damage caused to trees by all of these mammals sometimes makes them a menace to forestry in certain areas.

Fungi, such as mushrooms, and lichens are not used much by mammals as a staple diet, although deer and rodents do eat them when they are obtainable, and red squirrels have been observed to impale mushrooms on branches as a reserve food supply for later consumption. Nuts are commonly eaten by many mammals, especially rodents and some primates. Squirrels are particularly fond of hazelnuts, which they open by gnawing a hole in the shell with the lower incisors. Deer and black bears, among other species, often feast on acorns and beechnuts after they have fallen to the ground in the fall. The molar teeth of primates are well adapted to cracking nuts, and they are an item in the diet of many monkeys.

The so-called ruminants, or cud-chewing ungulates, have an interesting specialization in regard to the intake of their food—herbaceous plants and foliage. The placid, meditative chewing, as if on a specially satisfying brand of gum,

DIET AND TEETH

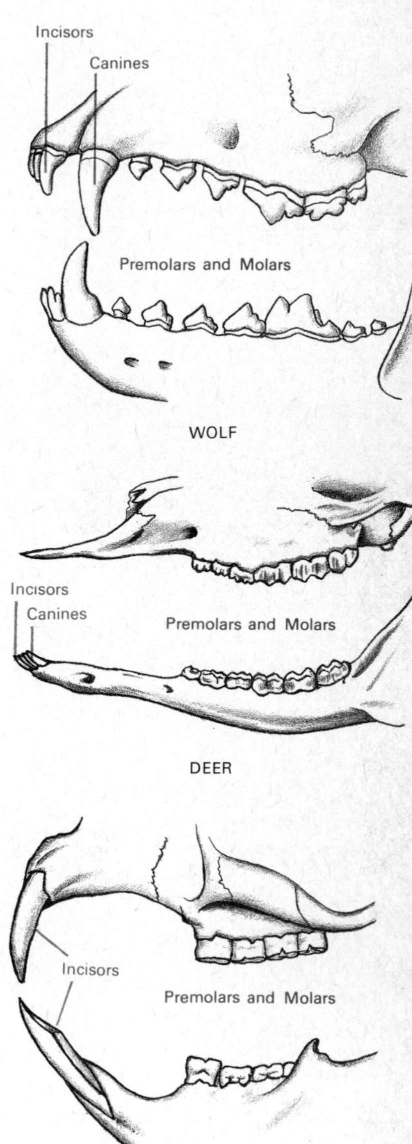

Three adaptations of teeth, reflecting three different kinds of diet, are shown above. The larger, sharp canines of the carnivorous wolf are used for stabbing and tearing meat, while its premolars and molars have been adapted for shearing rather than grinding. In the deer, a ruminant, grinding teeth predominate. The canines and incisors in the upper jaw have been replaced by a horny pad, used with the lower front teeth for cropping vegetation. The porcupine, a typical rodent, has no canines at all. Its most prominent teeth are the long, self-sharpening incisors used for gnawing.

practiced by cows and some other hoofed mammals is familiar to all visitors to the countryside, but not everyone knows exactly what is going on. The living ruminants have exceptionally complicated stomachs, usually provided with four chambers to handle the difficult task of digesting their completely vegetarian diets. Food taken into the mouth is briefly chewed, then swallowed almost whole and stored in the first stomach, or "rumen." Here a rich flora of bacteria acts upon it and prepares it for digestion. After the process is continued in a second stomach compartment, the "reticulum," the resultant pulp is returned to the mouth for further leisurely mastication. Only then is it passed to the third and fourth stomach compartments, where it is completely broken down to provide the nourishment the animal needs.

The extremely specialized diets of some mammals sometimes place them in grave danger of starving. A classic example is the koala of Australia, which can survive only on certain species of eucalyptus leaves. Similarly, the red tree mouse of the northwestern United States cannot subsist except on the needles and young shoots of the Douglas fir. The evolutionary disadvantages of such specializations in diet are obvious and largely account for the fact that species unable to adopt new feeding habits are today in danger of extinction.

RUMINANT DIGESTION

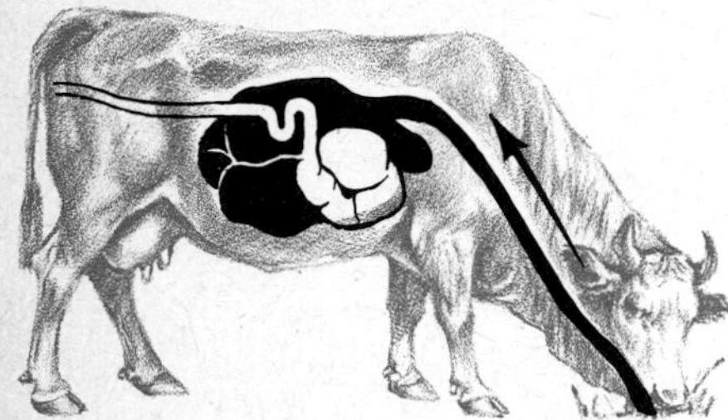

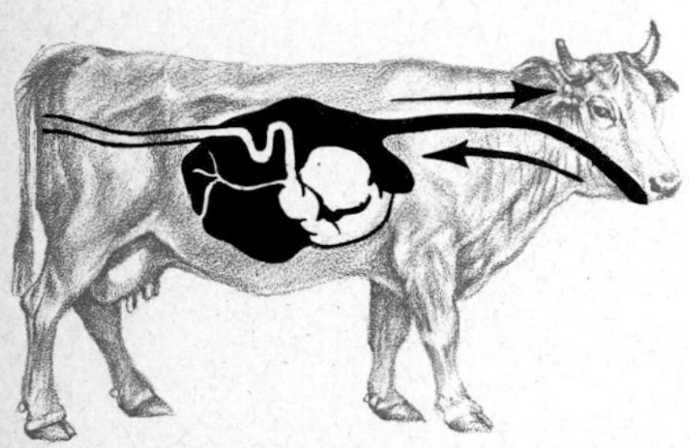

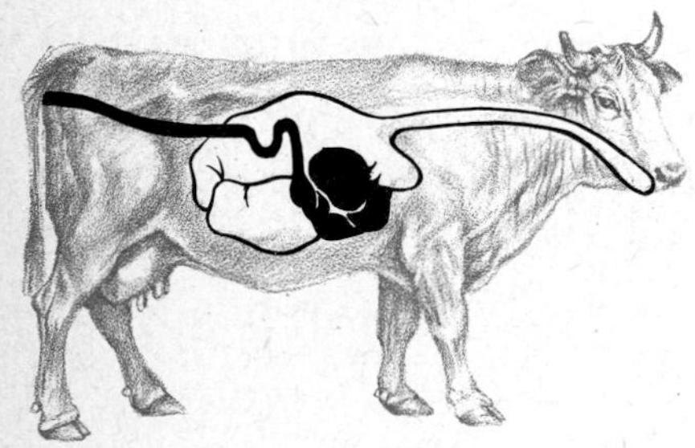

The progress of food through the four stomach chambers of a cow is indicated in black in the pictures above. The vegetation is swallowed only partly chewed. It goes into two connecting chambers, the rumen and the reticulum (top picture), where it is broken down into pulp by bacteria and later regurgitated as cud (middle picture). After rechewing, it is passed to two other chambers, the omasum and the abomasum (bottom picture). In the latter it is worked on by gastric juices before entering the intestine, through which the nutriment is absorbed. Grass passes through the animal in about 24 hours, but rougher forage may take up to seven days.

A DIFFERENT kind of problem facing vegetarian mammals is exemplified by the elephant. Because of its great size, this animal needs a very large supply of food indeed if it is to maintain its body machinery in proper working order. A full-grown male African elephant may weigh as much as six tons, and in a wild state even an elephant of much more modest proportions needs to consume between 300 and 400 pounds of rough fodder each day. To achieve this enormous intake, the animal's life is virtually transformed into one long meal, for it must browse intermittently all day long if it is to be fully nourished.

Although the elephants are an extreme case, vegetarian mammals normally feed for much longer periods than carnivores. This is due to their position in the "food chains" which are of such fundamental importance in the economy of nature. At the bottom of a chain are the green plants which, as we have said, use the energy provided by the sun to create more complicated compounds from the simple chemicals in the air and soil. When eaten by herbivorous animals, some of the stored energy of the plants in turn becomes concentrated in the bodies of these animals. Last in the chain come the carnivores, which are adapted for preying on the vegetarians. By doing this, they receive their vital energy in exceptionally concentrated form, for the earlier stages of synthesis have already been done for them. Thus when we eat a leg of mutton for dinner we are absorbing not a simple substance but a concentrate of the stored energy which the sheep has previously extracted from the thousands of plants that built its body to its present succulent state. These facts help us to understand why the feeding habits of carnivores are so fundamentally different from those of their vegetarian cousins; why a cat or a dog, for instance, can subsist quite happily on one meal a day, while the elephant has to keep stoking up its engines with a continuous supply of fuel.

The problem of obtaining food is generally more complicated for carnivores than for vegetarians, however. Carnivores have to work for their living much harder than the vegetarians, and greater demands are normally made on their intelligence if they are to survive.

Among the most efficient of all carnivores are the members of the cat family, which has spread to almost every region of the world and has enjoyed a great evolutionary success. Two African cats, the cheetah and the lion, provide good examples of the techniques used by these carnivores to obtain their food.

The cheetah, found in both Africa and Asia, has a slim build and exceptionally long legs. The world's fastest land mammal, it feeds largely on small antelopes and gazelles, which are likewise capable of very fast movement. When it spots a herd of grazing gazelles, its technique is to move slowly toward them, facing the wind, "freezing" immediately if it has any suspicion that they may be looking its way. As soon as it is close enough, the cheetah will suddenly rush forward with maximum energy and, in many cases, will be on the quarry before the latter has had time even to realize its danger.

The lion is more heavily built than the cheetah and not so speedy. It therefore often relies more on guile and cooperative effort when hunting its prey—usually zebras or such large antelopes as gnus, hartebeests and elands. Many observers have reported that lions often hunt in pairs, the male simply alarming the game so that it stampedes into the jaws of the waiting female.

All carnivorous mammals normally fear man, but on certain occasions both lions and tigers, and even some of the smaller cats, have been known to turn man-eater. The taste for human flesh is probably acquired by the success of some chance attack, which thereafter causes the animal to lose its fear of our species and to take to a diet of human flesh. Very old lions and tigers which have become incapable of catching more active game may also be driven in desperation to become habitual man-eaters. Whatever the cause, man-eating in cats seems to go in epidemics. This may be because the parent cats, once having broken down their inhibitions about attacking man, give their cubs the chance to taste human flesh. Then, when the cubs grow up, the whole family of lions or tigers may begin to terrorize a district.

AFTER the cats, the weasel and dog families contain the greatest number of carnivores. Dogs hunt their prey in quite a different way from cats, however, and do not normally resort to such techniques as stalking or ambush. They rely much more than cats on cooperative effort, and several families will combine in winter into a troop or pack to obtain their quarry. For example, the wild hunting dogs of Africa move in packs some 20 to 30 strong, preceded by their leader, who scouts ahead at a distance of several hundred yards. When he sights a herd of game, he does not attempt to use any subtle stalking technique, but immediately gets it on the run and attempts to outflank it. With his immense speed he will usually succeed in getting ahead of any stragglers and turning them into the jaws of the pack, which is now running behind and on the opposite side, waiting. The sustained effort required for such long periods of running, culminating in a tussle with a desperate quarry, is quite beyond the abilities of any member of the cat family. These two groups of mammals, therefore, illustrate very nicely the range of specializations which can be made by different predators in acquiring the same kind of food.

Dogs and cats are the best-known carnivorous mammals, but there are, of course, many other forms which are specialized for capturing and eating particular kinds of prey. There are, for instance, the carnivores habitually dwelling in or near water. The majority of adult seals and sea lions are voracious fisheaters, although the young are often partial to prawns and other marine invertebrates. The common seal, found in northern waters, will eat between 10 and 12 pounds of fish each day. Such a diet makes it unpopular with fishing communities, even though most of its food consists of "rough" fish not used by man. The so-called crabeater seal of the antarctic has a more specialized diet, which consists mainly of crustaceans. Several other species of seals eat octopus and squid. The torpedo-shaped bodies of these animals are particularly well adapted for swift movement through water—a vital necessity in pursuing their aquatic prey.

Seals and sea lions are near the top of their particular food chains, but they themselves are sometimes the victims, not the victors, of the chase. Polar bears are particularly fond of seal meat, which they obtain in a variety of ways. They may stalk the seals across the ice floes where they sometimes emerge to doze; a sudden rush and a blow from the front paw will then usually secure the prey, for the flippered limbs of seals make them as ungainly on land as they are agile in the water. Sometimes the bears ambush their quarry at the breathing holes which the seals keep open in the ice. More rarely, they capture the seals in the water by swimming among the floes.

MAMMALS THAT CATCH FISH

RIVER OTTER

Mammals often use more than one method to exploit the same type of food, as demonstrated by these three fisheaters. The otter hunts them down in their own element. Long and slim with a streamlined body and webbed feet, it is a superb swimmer and can catch any small fish with ease. It brings its catch onto dry land to eat.

Otters, like seals and sea lions, are great fisheaters, and their bodies are similarly streamlined. They will, however, eat many other foods, such as crustaceans, small amphibians and reptiles, and the fledglings of water birds that come their way. One species, the sea otter, has taken almost exclusively to marine life, ranging along the Pacific coasts and offshore islands from the Bering Sea to California. The sea otter sleeps moored to floating beds of seaweed. It feeds mainly on crabs, sea urchins and mollusks, and one of its favorite foods in California waters is the hard-shelled red abalone. It often opens shellfish in a most original way: floating on its back with a stone lying on its chest, it cracks the shells of bivalves or sea urchins by pounding them on the stone.

Apart from such strictly aquatic species, several other mammals take much of their food from the rivers, lakes and oceans. For instance, the fishing cat of tropical Asia is adept at hooking fish from rivers with its forepaws, while some large hare-lipped, or bulldog, bats of tropical America snatch the same prey from just below the surface with their heavily clawed hind feet.

One of the most extreme physical specializations to a particular diet is shown by the various species of anteaters. The most spectacular member of the group is the giant anteater of South and Central America, which may measure six feet from nose to tail. The head is shaped like a long tube, which enables it to be projected deep into ant and termite nests in which a hole has previously been torn by the strong, curved claws. Even in the region of the eyes and ears, the head is only three or four inches across, and the snout, which is about 20 inches long, is scarcely an inch broad at the tip. Here there is no "mouth" as we generally understand the word, but a small hole through which the sticky, wormlike tongue can be extruded as much as 15 inches. The scurrying ants stick to the surface of the tongue, which is then withdrawn. In this way the giant anteater can consume several thousands of ants at a single meal, and the stomach of dissected specimens have sometimes contained masses of half-digested ants weighing well over a pound.

Several mammals of quite different orders have practiced similar feeding habits with great success, among them the marsupial banded "anteater" of Australia and the long-beaked echidna from New Guinea. The echidna is a monotreme, and therefore no more closely related to the true anteater than its marsupial neighbor, but its long tubelike snout and sticky tongue show a marked functional similarity to those of the giant anteater of America. This fact emphasizes the well-established evolutionary principle of convergence, in which similar adaptations are frequently made by animals belonging to quite different groups as an answer to comparable challenges in the environment.

One question of particular interest concerning mammals and their food is the extent to which, in a situation where suitable food is abundant and varied, they discriminate between the actual *taste* of one food and another. We all know that a dog will select favorite morsels from its dinner plate before eating the rest. But then this is an artificial situation, and the dog has been profoundly influenced by man over a long period. The gastronomic preferences of wild animals are more difficult to discover.

Judging from their behavior, elephants certainly do have such preferences. Around the slopes of Mount Kenya, there is still a large elephant population and also a rich supply of the vegetable foods these animals need. Yet every January and February large numbers of elephants migrate to the higher slopes of the mountain, where at this time the berries of the mukaita tree come into season. The fact that they gorge themselves on these with obvious enjoyment and then descend again certainly suggests that they make this annual trip for purely gastronomic reasons.

Other examples of this trait in elephants are more reprehensible. For instance, the naturalist David Blunt has reported a case of a wild African elephant which acquired such a passion for fermented millet that it would make determined nightly raids on a native village to obtain it. Another case is cited by the 19th Century hunter W. H. Drummond, who observed the seasonal migrations of elephants in Pongolo in search of the fruit of the umganu tree. "This fruit is capable of being made into a strong intoxicating drink," he wrote, "and the elephants after eating it became quite tipsy, staggering about, playing huge antics, screaming so as to be heard miles off, and not seldom having tremendous fights." Man is therefore probably not the only mammal to discriminate between the taste—and effects—of different foods in addition to needing them as an essential to survival.

HARE-LIPPED BAT

The hare-lipped bat of tropical America swoops over patches of water where small fish rest at night just beneath the surface. It catches them by raking, apparently at random, with its elongated claws. The Asian fishing cat (below) crouches on the bank and when a fish comes within range it scoops it up with a webbed forepaw.

FISHING CAT

ANOTHER aspect of mammalian feeding habits which is reminiscent of man is the instinct of some species to establish hoards of food in times of plenty which can be used later when supplies are more difficult to get.

Chipmunks and some deer mice stuff seeds or nuts into their cheek pouches and carry them to their storerooms, where they lay them away against hard times. Gray squirrels hide nuts in crevices and bury them all over the forest floor; some of these nuts are dug up later and eaten, but many are forgotten and may eventually sprout and become trees. The little harelike pika, or "haymaker," of the Rocky Mountains, cures cut grass in the sun, then drags it into piles under sheltered ledges where it will be available when the area is covered with snow.

Besides these, mammals as different as bears, moles and even leopards are all known to establish "larders" of different kinds. The same instinct can be observed in the domestic dog when it buries a half-finished bone in the garden. Bears, wolves and some foxes often bury the remains of partially eaten food, and some other carnivores kill and secrete prey in an intact condition. One example is the red fox of the northern plains of the United States, which in winter makes caches of food in the snow and in summer covers the carcasses of its prey with a layer of light soil. Leopards often take the entrails and limbs of their victim as a first meal and hide the rest in thick cover or even drag it up a tree and lodge it in a forked branch. Among smaller mammals, certain moles are renowned for their hoarding instincts, and stocks of a thousand or more earthworms have sometimes been found in their burrows. The mole will first bite the worm near the front of its body, which immobilizes the creature yet keeps it alive and fresh for future consumption. Moles, incidentally, are voracious eaters, and some have been known to consume their own weight in food every 24 hours.

Apart from the specializations found in the teeth, snouts and claws of different mammals, various other adaptations often help a mammal to obtain food. The tongue of the anteater has already been mentioned, and the tongues of many other mammals are likewise adapted to their special diets. One example is the long, black, flexible tongue of the giraffe, which can be extended and deftly wrapped round the tender leaves and shoots of trees. Another is the extremely rough tongue of the cats, which is as harsh as a file and obviously assists the animals in licking flesh from bones.

Another interesting specialization, usually associated with reptiles rather than mammals, is the use of venom to kill, or at least to immobilize, the prey. Little work has been done on this subject, but there is sound evidence that certain shrews produce poisonous secretions similar to snake venom from their submaxillary salivary glands. Shrews had long been suspected of being venomous in Europe, but in the first case of shrew poisoning recorded in North America, Mr. C. J. Maynard reported in 1889 that he had been bitten on the hand by a short-tailed shrew which he had picked up. Within a few seconds he began to experience burning sensations, swelling and shooting pains in his hand and arm. For three days he could not use his hand without great pain. In 1942 the naturalist O. P. Pearson proved by experiment that venom from the glands of the short-tailed shrew caused a lowering of the blood pressure, a slowing of the heart and inhibition of breathing when injected into mice. In such victims, the venom is capable of producing a state of semitorpor in less than a minute. There seems to be little doubt that this shrew usually uses its poison to incapacitate prey, which it can then kill and eat without any further struggle.

ARE there any lessons to be learned from the eating habits of mammals which will illumine the nature of the evolutionary process as a whole? As we have seen, many mammals are highly specialized feeders, and their physical equipment is often excellently adapted to help them obtain their chosen diet. Such creatures have often enjoyed long periods of successful development, but one must remember that they are always at the mercy of their various specialized food supplies. If these diminish, the very adaptations of physique which once gave the particular animal an evolutionary advantage are no longer of special benefit and may even become a handicap. How, for instance, would the lion or the tiger, both creatures totally unfitted for a herbivorous diet, manage to get a living if there was a rapid reduction in herbivorous game? And how would the herbivores themselves survive if a change in climate caused the flora of their homelands to change in a radical way? In such situations of sudden challenge, which have often occurred in the history of life, it is the creatures that can readily adapt themselves to a wide *range* of foods that have the greatest chance of survival. Certainly the immense success of the brown rat, which today has a nearly worldwide distribution, is closely connected with its ability to eat almost anything that comes its way, from wax candles to lizards, and from insects and garbage to the seeds of plants. And even in the advanced mammal we call man the same principle applies. It is the enormous *adaptability* of our species, in diet as in so many other directions, that has been a major factor in bringing it to the domination of the earth.

TWO YOUNG AFRICAN LIONS FINISH OFF A ZEBRA CARCASS. LIONS RARELY FIGHT OVER A KILL, AND KILL ONLY WHAT THEY NEED TO EAT

Diet and Survival

Both the shape of an animal and its habits are inseparably linked with the kind of food it eats. As the environment and the food supply slowly change over long periods of time, animals will tend to change too. Generally speaking, species that are not too closely tied to one food source or to one specialized method of eating will have the best chance for continued survival through adaptation.

THE FLAT GRINDERS of a herbivore, much reduced, may be seen at the back of the mouth of this hippopotamus. Its other teeth are more specialized. The blunt incisors jutting from the lower jaw aid the lips in obtaining vegetation. The tusklike lower canines have become adapted as effective weapons. When the mouth is shut they fit into sheathlike pockets in the upper jaw.

Three Kinds of Teeth

Except for some special cases, mammals generally tackle their food in one of three ways—by gnawing, by grinding or by tearing—and their teeth have become adapted accordingly. Rodents, which must gnaw through seed cases and nutshells, have upper and lower pairs of sharply curved, prominent front teeth that continue growing throughout life so that constant use will not wear them down to stumps. Herbivores, which subsist largely on grasses, usually have flat-topped premolars and molars, with abrasive grinding surfaces for thorough chewing. Carnivores generally tear at their food with prominent, sharp canines and bolt it down in chunks. Their molars and premolars are adapted as shearing teeth.

LONG RODENT INCISORS distinguish an Alpine marmot. With front surfaces of hard enamel, they are backed by softer dentine, so that constant gnawing keeps them sharpened like chisels.

THE SHARP TEETH of a carnivore, with conspicuous canines, are revealed by the coyote above. They accompany other carnivorous characteristics useful in capturing prey: powerful jaws, alertness, and acuteness of sight, smell and hearing. Since meat eaters do little chewing, some of their molars have degenerated and others are adapted for shearing meat and crunching bones.

WITH LEGS SPLAYED, two giraffes take an awkward drink. Before lowering themselves into this position, giraffes generally look carefully around,

Feeding Habits and Structure

The different kinds of animal teeth are only one example of the many ways in which physical structure is linked with diet. These adaptations take innumerable forms: the sharp teeth of the predators; the front paws that enable rodents to hold and bury nuts and seeds; and the complicated digestive mechanism of the ruminants, which permits the inclusion in their diets of vegetation that would otherwise be indigestible. More specialized examples are the long sticky tongue of the anteater, the fringed plates of the baleen whale that act as strainers for the huge amounts of plankton it eats daily, and the walrus tusks that are so efficiently adapted for digging up mollusks.

The nature of the adaptation always

THE LONG NECK and long legs of the giraffe make it the tallest animal on earth. Some individuals are more than 19 feet in height. The preferred food of giraffes is the young leaves and shoots at the tops of acacia trees.

because the slowness with which they can straighten up again makes them extremely vulnerable to attack by their principal enemy, the African lion.

depends upon the particular animal and its circumstances; there is no single perfect solution, even to the same problem. The long neck of the giraffe and the long trunk of the elephant are about as different solutions as could possibly be found to the problem of reaching high for food. It is incorrect to say, of course, that either was developed *for the purpose* to which it is now put. The neck and trunk both came gradually out of an extremely subtle process of adaptation which depended partly on the opportunities offered by the environment and partly on the characteristics that the animal already had. Elephants simply could not now grow long necks, for example, since their heads have become far too large and too heavy.

WITH TRUNK RAISED, an elephant reaches for some tender shoots. Besides plucking leaves, twigs and fruit from trees, the trunk can pull grass, carry water to the mouth and test the air for smells of food or danger.

A NECTAR EATER'S tongue may be a fourth as long as its owner. Nectar droplets cling to the tip when it is withdrawn from a flower.

Bloodsuckers and Nectar Drinkers

In evolution there is only one criterion for measuring the "success" of a species or a group of species and that is whether or not it continues to survive. Survival is not certain for any organism, but it is made more likely by such circumstances as large numbers and wide distribution, and by a process known as adaptive radiation—the branching out of one group of animals into a variety of niches that the parent type did not previously occupy. The bats, for example, started out as insect eaters, and although the majority are still insectivorous, there are now bats that live on fruit, fish, nectar, blood, rodents, frogs and even other bats. With this great variability in their way of life, bats have become the second largest mammalian order and are now spread over most of the globe. In the course of this radiation process the different species have become greatly modified in structure and habits.

HOVERING LIKE A HUMMINGBIRD, A LONG-NOS

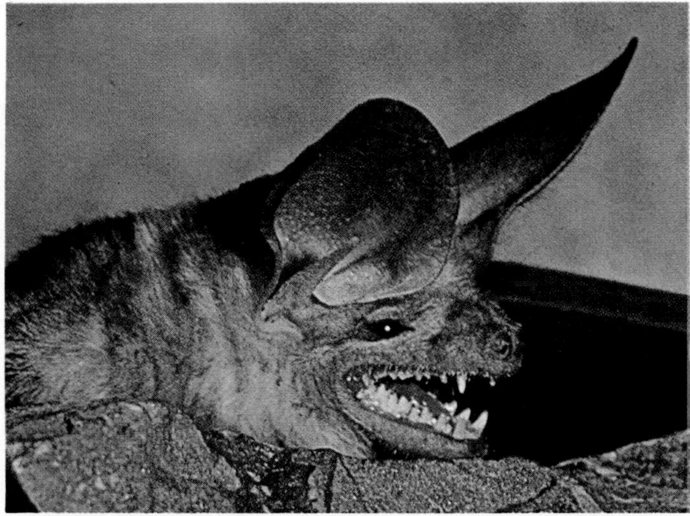

AN INSECT EATER, the pallid bat locates prey by emitting shrill squeaks and picking up echoes reflected from flying insects.

A FISH-EATING BAT, *Pizonyx* chews a recent catch. It uses its elongated claws to snatch fish while it swoops over the water.

BAT PROBES FOR NECTAR IN A NIGHT-BLOOMING CACTUS BLOSSOM. THESE NIGHT FLIERS POLLINATE FLOWERS JUST AS DAY-FLYING HUMMINGBIRDS DO

A BLOOD DRINKER, the vampire bat gently scrapes the skin of sleeping mammals and birds, and laps up the oozing blood.

A FRUIT EATER enjoys a mouthful of berries. These bats locate food mainly by smell, while the insect eaters use echo sounding.

A GRASSHOPPER MOUSE ENJOYS ITS USUAL MEAL

The Flexible Feeders

While the bats as a group prosper through the ability of different species to exploit different food sources, there are other mammals that do just the opposite. These are the omnivores, whose great survival asset is that individual animals can eat a wide variety of foods. Omnivore literally means "eat all things," and the advantage that this ability confers is obvious. Bears, for example, change their diet to conform to the bounty of the seasons. They gorge on fish when the salmon are running in the rivers, on berries in berrytime, and on honey, grubs, beetles, frogs and small mammals whenever they come across them. Other well-known omnivores are foxes, coyotes, opossums and raccoons. The raccoon will eat almost anything and is an accomplished forager of garbage dumps.

What is not so well known is that many other mammals fall in this category. Deer and rabbits both eat meat at times, and some of the rodents are steady meat eaters. The grasshopper mouse eats a wide variety of insects and caterpillars. A fifth of its diet is grasshoppers, and it will even kill and eat other small mice and voles when it can. It falls back on seeds only when animal food is scarce. Aside from man, the most outstanding omnivore of all is the brown rat, which will even eat its own kind.

WALNUT ON THE HALF SHELL furnishes a snack for a European red squirrel. The bright-eyed rodent favors pine seeds and hazelnuts, but it eats acorns, toadstools and birds' eggs as well.

PERSIMMONS, CORN AND FISH provide three different menus for the three raccoons above. Their diets are further varied by small mammals, birds and reptiles, as well as nuts and seeds.

A HUNGRY OTTER finds a fishing hole in the ice. Otters usually travel by swimming, but when rivers freeze they must walk.

Hunger and Hard Times

In cold weather, when food is difficult or impossible to come by, some animals escape the problem of eating entirely by hibernating. For others, winter can be a time of hardship and starvation.

The food of the herbivore is often buried under deep drifts and can only be gotten at by ranging widely to find spots blown bare by the wind or by digging down to it. Bighorn sheep may migrate to lower levels on the mountains as winter sets in.

A COYOTE HOPEFULLY EXAMINES THE SKELETON OF AN ELK WHICH HAS ALREADY BEEN PICKED ALMOST CLEAN BY EARLIER SCAVENGERS. COYOTES,

Deer and moose try to keep "yards" trampled down in the forests in order to have a little browse available during blizzards. Bison drift before storms, and although they are powerful animals, they sometimes founder and starve in chest-deep snow. For the carnivore, pickings are slim. Many of its normal victims are hibernating and cannot be found. Those that are up and about are not producing young—an important food source at other times.

EVEN IN GOOD TIMES, WILL EAT CARRION AS WELL AS FRESH-KILLED PREY

ROOTING IN THE SNOW, a bison forages for the short grass that grows beneath. Bison can break through heavily crusted snow, and will butt through ice with their heads to obtain water.

PAWING THE SNOW ASIDE, a reindeer uncovers the winter lichen essential to its survival. One animal consumes about 25 pounds a day, and herds must keep moving to obtain supplies.

A CARIBOU SKELETON is investigated for further morsels by three wolf cubs, one with its head in the rib cage. Normally fresh-meat eaters, wolves will accept carrion in hard times.

A FAT EARTHWORM is caught by a star-nosed mole. Some European moles store large supplies of live worms after paralyzing them by biting them.

The Food Storers

Better off than the scavengers and the seasonal migrants are the hoarders, which make provision for the hard months by gathering and storing the food that is abundant during the warmer seasons. Many carnivores bury temporary caches of game to return to later; in the arctic regions polar bears, foxes and wolves keep surplus meat in cold storage on the frozen ground or in the snow. But the most systematic hoarders are small burrowing animals, and rodents like chipmunks, beavers and squirrels. Pine squirrels regularly assemble mounds of pine cones several feet across. And the little pikas are as methodical as any farmer in getting in hay, drying it and storing it. However, they do not put it under cover during showers, as some people think.

A SUPPLY OF GRASS for the winter is gathered by a pika in the three pictures at left. In the bottom one, it scatters its load on the haystack. Each day's layer is spread thinly on top of the previous one to dry.

ITS CHEEKS BULGING, a chipmunk holds 93 ragweed seeds. Cheek pouches are useful to a small hoarder; they cut down the number of dangerous trips it has to make between food source and storage chamber.

THREATENING POSTURE of an Alaskan timber wolf, with head down, fangs bared and hackles bristling, is an unmistakable signal for others to defer or keep away. Actual fights among members of the pack are rare.

5

Attack, Defense and Survival

THE battle for life makes it necessary for all mammals to have offensive and defensive adaptations. In predators the power to attack and kill is essential to survival; in their prey there is an equally urgent need to avoid or repel the hunter. The same capacities are needed in the often fierce competition for mates. Efficiency in attack and defense is, in fact, one of the most fundamental requirements of any animal.

In mammals, attack and defense are exemplified in many different forms. First there are the actual physical structures—teeth and claws, for example, or armor and quills—which have obvious offensive or defensive functions. Less obvious physical specializations are such devices as the foul-smelling glandular secretions of skunks, the capacity of certain mammals to shed parts of their tails, as lizards do, if these are grasped by a predator, and various camouflaging or warning colors. Yet a third expression of a mammal's offensive or defensive abilities is not connected with physical structure at all, but with behavior. Here we can cite such reactions as flight, "freezing" into a rigid position, "playing possum" and so on. Many mammals are equipped with specializations in all three of these categories.

2 YEARS

6 YEARS

12 YEARS

THE GROWTH OF HORNS

Horns first appear in the bighorn as small, hard "buttons" when the young ram is about eight weeks old. They grow rapidly the first year and with increasing slowness thereafter, the ends curling downward until in an old ram they may describe a complete circle. Each year a ridge of new growth appears at the base of the horn. Determining the age of the ram from these ridges is risky because after six or eight years they run together and become so wrinkled that it is hard to count them.

The horns of antelopes and the antlers of deer are particularly obvious examples of weapons possessed by mammals. Although comparable in function, they differ considerably in structure. Horns, usually possessed by both sexes, are permanent features which continue to grow throughout the animal's life. They consist of bony processes jutting out from the skull, covered with a hard substance known as keratin, which is actually tougher than bone. Keratin is also found in other mammalian structures such as the skin, claws, hoofs, hair and fingernails.

Antlers, by contrast, are composed of pure bone and are shed and regenerated seasonally. With the exception of reindeer and caribou, in which they occur in both sexes, they are normally grown only by male deer. The main function of antlers seems to be connected with sexual selection, for they are at the peak of their efficiency during the mating season, when rival males are fighting for the possession of females. Antlers vary greatly in size and design, ranging from the elaborate branching structures grown by moose and wapiti to the much simpler antlers characteristic of many smaller species. In fact, antler size seems to be very largely correlated with the body size of the animal. Such small deer as the pudu of the Chilean Andes and the tufted deer of China have antlers which are only half-inch spikes, while Chinese water deer have no antlers at all. They are equipped instead with greatly elongated upper canine teeth, or tusks.

There is considerable variation in the horns of wild cattle, sheep and goats. Cape buffalo, for example, have massive side-sweeping horns that curve outward and then upward at the ends. The musk ox has hooked horns that sweep downward and then up, while the little Celebes anoa has almost straight horns, which are directed backward. The wild sheep usually have horns that curve in a tight spiral, those of the Rocky Mountain bighorn often making a complete circle or more. The horns of wild goats are generally simple curves, but they often feature twists or spirals as well.

EVEN greater variations of design are found in the horns of antelopes. There are the rapierlike horns of the oryx, the sweeping, crescent-shaped horns of the giant sable, the double-curved horns of the impala, the little spiky horns of the duiker and the exceptionally large corkscrew horns of the kudu. Many other antelopes possess horns quite different from any of those mentioned.

Quite apart from their use to their owners, horns and antlers are of great interest in themselves. The yearly growth of antlers is a particularly remarkable phenomenon which imposes a great strain on the animals producing them. The structures develop from two projections of the frontal bone, known as pedicels, which are normally concealed by the skin of the head, but in such deer as the muntjac they protrude in prominent fashion. The growing process takes up to five months and resembles that of typical bone formation, but because it has to take place so much more quickly, the animal utilizes far greater quantities of lime and phosphoric acid than would normally be the case.

Starting as simple swellings that bud and push out from the bony pedicels of the skull, the antlers rapidly increase in size and in many species they branch repeatedly as they grow. At this time the antlers may be bent or deformed very easily, for they are composed of flexible bony material enclosed in a covering of soft skin covered with fine hair, called "velvet." A network of blood vessels in the velvet nourishes the antlers until they reach full growth and then ossification proceeds from the base until the complete structures become rigid and formidable symbols of their owner's virility. Finally, the velvet peels off, a process which the stag hastens by rubbing his antlers against trees and rocks or even against the ground. A little blood may appear at this time, derived from the blood vessels lying beneath the velvet. It is the drying up of these blood vessels which causes the velvet to peel, and their former channels can be seen as well-defined grooves in the completed antler.

After the breeding season, the antlers are shed. A little blood usually appears again when each antler drops from its pedicel, but this quickly dries and the surface heals over. Within several months, new buds appear and the next set of antlers begins its growth.

With each successive growth, the size and elaboration of the antlers increases for a number of years. Thus the first pair of antlers grown by a yearling white-tailed deer are small and simple spikes. The following year they are bigger and more complex. In the European red deer, nine successive growths and sheddings are sometimes necessary before the antlers appear in their full glory; even the smaller roe and fallow deer need from five to six years for their antlers to become fully mature. For several years thereafter, provided the animals have an equivalent food supply each year, the antlers remain fairly constant in size and shape. But when the animal passes his full prime of sexual vigor, the antlers begin to degenerate in size and quality.

BESIDES such weapons as horns and antlers, the teeth of mammals are widely used for attack and defense. Mammalian teeth differ greatly from those of the reptiles from which they evolved. Reptiles characteristically possess a battery of peglike teeth, each of which—except in such cases as the fangs of poisonous snakes—is generally little differentiated from the next. Mammals, by contrast, have evolved much more specialized teeth, which, as stated earlier, can be broadly classified into three groups: incisors, canines and cheek teeth. The use of these teeth in eating has already been discussed, but in many cases they are of at least equal value as offensive and defensive weapons. The general value of teeth for almost any animal in attack and defense is too obvious to emphasize, but some of the adaptations they have acquired for these activities are of particular interest.

The most typical offensive specialization in mammalian teeth is represented by the canines. There are usually two of these sharp, elongated teeth, both in the upper and the lower jaw, and they are excellent natural daggers. Canines are essential to such typical predators as lions and tigers in dealing with their prey and are also well developed as a deterrent to aggressors in nonpredators such as the gorilla. One of their most extreme specializations occurred in the extinct saber-toothed cats. But various mammals living today have canine teeth which are just as remarkable.

The tusks of the walrus are simple, highly developed canines. Apart from being used for digging up mollusks from the bed of the sea, these teeth are used by both sexes in defending themselves against such predators as polar bears and by the bull walruses in fighting rivals at mating time. The hides of old specimens are often formidably scarred by the tusk marks inflicted during these ferocious combats.

Another instance of teeth which have become specialized into tusks occurs in the elephant. But unlike the walrus' tusks, the tusks of elephants have not been developed from the canines, but from the incisors. Elephants when fighting are capable of inflicting dreadful wounds with their tusks, even to the extent of disemboweling their opponents. The tusks are also of value in protecting young

THE GROWTH OF ANTLERS

Unlike horns, antlers of a male white-tailed deer are formed and shed every year. As shown above, they push out from the bony pedicels on the skull in early spring and are not fully developed until the fall breeding season, when the buck rubs off their velvet covering and polishes them against the trunks of saplings. In a fight it will try to push its opponent off balance and gore it. After the rutting period is over, from mid-December to February, the antlers fall off, ordinarily one at a time.

members of a herd from the large cats, which are always ready to attack an elephant calf if opportunity offers. The only creature against whom the tusks can offer no defense is man. With his powerful rifles he can kill an elephant from a distance of several hundred yards, and between 2,000 and 5,000 elephants have been destroyed annually in recent times in Kenya alone by sportsmen and ivory poachers.

As a final example of mammals possessing specialized weapon teeth, we may cite two members of the pig family: the wart hog and the babirussa. In the male, or boar, wart hog the canines of the upper jaw turn upward and may attain a length of 8 to 10 inches. With this equipment it can defend itself and its family from the attack of all but the largest and most formidable predators. The babirussa, from the Celebes and parts of the Moluccas, is even better equipped, for the canines of the lower jaw are also well developed and grow in the same direction as the upturned canines of the upper jaw. These upper canines actually grow through the roof of the snout. Besides the aggressive possibilities of this battery of specialized teeth, they also provide a protective cage which effectively screens the upper part of the face.

AN ARMOR-PLATED RUMP

Only six inches long, Chlamyphorus, the fairy armadillo of the Argentine pampas, is the smallest living armadillo. Unlike most of its relatives, it is furred and is only partially covered with a cape of scales attached along its backbone. If its sole defense were to roll up, it could be killed easily by predators. However, this armadillo also has a separate bony shield on its rump and an armored tail. It lives underground most of the time, emerging at night to feed on insects, grubs and vegetable matter. When frightened, it burrows quickly into the sandy soil, and its rear armor protects it while digging.

As a purely defensive structure, armor is particularly effective, and the bodies of various mammals have a protective covering which makes it difficult for predators to get at the vital organs. The thick skins of elephants and rhinoceroses are armor of a kind, but the very bulk of the creatures also plays a major part in discouraging attack. More highly specialized armor is found in several smaller mammals, especially the armadillos and pangolins. Covered with thick plates, some armadillos can roll themselves into a ball so that their soft parts are virtually inaccessible even to the most persistent predators. Others ward off attacks by pressing themselves flat on the ground beneath the arch of rigid plates which covers their backs. One of the most remarkable armadillos is scientifically known as *Chlamyphorus truncatus*. In addition to the armored "cloak" that extends along the upper part of its body, this creature has its tail and hindquarters covered with a thick bony shield. If threatened, it bolts into its burrow and stops the entrance with its armored rear. The pangolins likewise have a protective covering of tough overlapping scales, or plates, and can roll themselves up at will. The female Indian pangolin has even been seen to envelop her young in her own protective covering when danger threatens.

Spines are another valuable means of defense, and the prickly surface of a rolled-up hedgehog is enough to deter most predators. Porcupines, however, possess the most formidable defensive structures of this kind. These animals, which may attain a length of two or more feet, live in both the Old and New Worlds. All are characterized by an array of quills on their backs, which can be raised by powerful muscles lying directly beneath the surface of the skin. This armament is most highly developed in the Old World forms. The common African porcupine, for instance, sometimes has quills as long as 15 inches.

When disturbed by a possible enemy, the African porcupine raises its quills and rubs them together to make a threatening sound. At the same time it makes grunting and snorting noises to show that it is not to be trifled with. If the annoyance persists, the porcupine charges swiftly backwards at its foe, with its quills held out like a battery of lances. If they make contact, many of the quills may become detached from the porcupine's back and remain embedded in the wounds they have made. This can have disastrous consequences to even the most powerful predator. There is one case on record of a tiger, almost fully

adult, that was killed by a porcupine whose quills perforated its liver and lungs during one of these aggressive-defensive maneuvers.

The quills of the Canadian porcupine are not so long, but they are just as effective, for they have barbed tips, which enable them—like fishhooks—to work their way deep into the victim's flesh. The average Canadian porcupine has some 30,000 of these barbed spikes, and any that become lost or broken are replaced. The mountain lion and fisher successfully prey on the porcupine by bowling the animal over and attacking its soft underbelly. Few other experienced predators venture to attack it. Dogs are frequent victims and so are the inexperienced young of other meat eaters.

An animal unfortunate enough to get a number of porcupine quills lodged in its flesh will be greatly distressed and may eventually die, for the quills continually work themselves deeper and deeper into the tissues. This occurs by muscular action on the barbs of the quills. The rate of penetration can be quite astonishing. A case is cited in the American *Journal of Mammalogy* of a quill fragment three quarters of an inch long which advanced almost two inches in just over a day.

Reinforcing the effect of offensive weapons and defensive armament is the concealing or warning coloration adopted by mammals. Rudyard Kipling in his story "How the Leopard Got His Spots" gives a delightful account of the principles of protective coloration in nature. In this story the giraffe, the zebra and the leopard, among other animals, were all reputed to live on the High Veldt and to be "sclusively sandy-yellow-brownish all over." But then, to avoid the leopard, the giraffe and the zebra retreated to the forests and acquired blotches and stripes from the broken shadows caused by the sun shining through the leaves. When the leopard followed them they were so perfectly camouflaged that they just melted into the forest with the words: "One-two-three! And where's your breakfast?" The leopard himself was then forced to acquire spots before he had a chance of hunting them on equal terms.

It would be wise not to trust Kipling too deeply about the way in which these protective colors were acquired, but his story does show how important camouflage can be to both predator and prey. The spotted pattern of the leopard does indeed conceal it most effectively in the wooded regions where it chiefly hunts. And many writers have commented on the way in which the zebra's stripes and the giraffe's blotches make these animals almost invisible in the thin cover where they habitually live, especially at dusk when an attack is most likely to occur. Thus one traveler, E. White Stewart, tells how on numerous occasions both he and his native tracker failed to observe zebra in scrub at distances of no more than 40 or 50 yards, and only detected them when they actually moved or switched their tails. Another traveler, Vaughn Kirby, writes of the giraffe: "The ghostly manner of their disappearance is most remarkable. I have often been riding up to them, when some other object has drawn my attention off for a few moments; glance again, and they are gone! Not merely gone to a distance though still in sight, but gone utterly, vanished like a mist-wreath at sunrise."

A striking example of the protective value of color is found in the variations which occur between local races of the same species of mammals. This subject has been studied in detail by Hugh Cott of Cambridge University, England, one of the world's leading authorities on animal camouflage. Cott has brought together a large body of evidence to show that the color variation in mammalian

A BATTERY OF QUILLS

The American porcupine's body and tail are spiked with loosely attached quills. Normally these lie flat, but when the animal is aroused they can be erected into a prickly battery of bristles. An attacker, whether from trying to bite the porcupine, from being swatted by its tail or from simply brushing against it, is immediately punctured by any quills it touches. These come loose from their owner, and thanks to the tiny barbs at their tips (below), not only get caught in the enemy, but actually continue to work in deeper and deeper through muscular action of the tissues in which they are embedded.

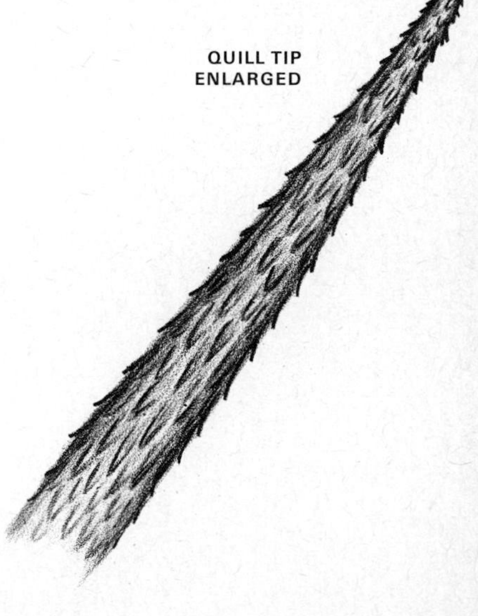

QUILL TIP ENLARGED

SEASONAL COLOR CHANGES OF A WEASEL'S COAT

APRIL

Through the long process of natural selection, a northern weasel now has the inborn capacity to exchange its summer coat of brown for one of winter white—and back again in spring. These molts are triggered by the changing day length. In March or April new dark hairs begin to appear on the weasel's back, gradually extending down the flanks until its upper parts are brown. The belly stays white.

MAY

races is almost certainly due to the elimination by predators of individuals that do not match their backgrounds as effectively as others. Thus in desert regions, many small mammals are a much lighter and sandier color than their close cousins, which may live in a darker environment. One race of pocket mice, which lives on the gypsum sand dunes of New Mexico's Tularosa Basin, is almost white. Another race of a closely related species inhabits dark lava flows in the same area and is almost totally black.

It seems certain that natural selection has been at work in such cases as these, eliminating the light forms from the dark-colored areas, and vice versa. Scientists have proved the point in controlled experiments, using different varieties of deer mice on different backgrounds. The barn owls and long-eared owls that were released in the rooms with them did indeed take more of the mice which did not blend with their backgrounds.

Certain arctic animals have year-round white coats which match the perpetual snow and ice of their environment. These include the polar bear, the northern races of the arctic hare and arctic wolf, and the Peary caribou of Ellesmere and other Canadian arctic islands. With various other northern mammals, such as the arctic fox, the varying hare and the short-tailed weasel, color variations are seasonal with the same individuals. These mammals often have a white coat in winter, but in summer assume a darker one.

The period during which the two coats are grown seems to be very closely correlated with the duration of total snow cover in the region. Thus the typical arctic fox of the far north alternates light and dark coats with the seasons, while members of the same species living in the less severe climatic environment of Iceland normally retain a dark coat the year round. Conversely, the local variant of the arctic hare which occurs on Ellesmere Island has a light coat throughout the year, while its cousin from the Hudson Bay region assumes a dark coat for some nine weeks in late summer when the snow is in retreat.

Although heredity plays a part in determining such changes of coat, experiments made with the snowshoe rabbit suggest that the length of daily illumination also has an important effect. The amount of light received through the eyes probably influences the pituitary gland, which in turn affects the hormones controlling the molting cycle.

BUT it is not only in the Arctic that mammals show a seasonal change in protective coloration. Another region where conditions vary greatly from one part of the year to the other is in the deciduous forests. Here in summer there is a thick canopy of leaves and a dappled pattern of sunshine and shadow is cast on the ground below. In winter this canopy disappears and a much more uniform light streams through the bare branches overhead. As we might expect, several mammals show protective adaptations to these changing conditions. To take only one example, the common fallow deer of Europe has a white-spotted coat in summer, which provides it with the same kind of concealment in this habitat as we have already described for the leopard. In winter, however, when spots would only make it more conspicuous, this coat is lost and the fur becomes a uniform grayish brown. The correlation of this species' seasonal coat changes with changes in the environment is supported by the fact that spotted deer living in tropical and subtropical evergreen forests do not go through such transformations. Thus the axis deer of Asia keeps its spots all the year round as a protective adaptation to the permanent leaf cover in its forest home.

In some mammals, bold warning colors rather than camouflage may serve

as an aid to survival and this is often achieved by the presence of conspicuous color patterns which contrast with the green and brown background of nature. Such patterns are generally associated with some dangerous or repellent characteristic and therefore act as a warning that aggression will bring unpleasant consequences.

The skunks are striking examples of this particular defensive device. These familiar American mammals are represented by three distinct genera, all of which possess coats of striking black-and-white patterns. All are also well known for their ability to emit a powerful odor when angry or frightened. This originates in their anal glands, which secrete a foul-smelling substance that can be projected with remarkable accuracy to a distance of 10 to 12 feet.

It seems quite clear that the skunk's specialized and particularly unpleasant defensive weapon is closely correlated with its conspicuous markings. These are simply a warning advertisement which says, in effect, to a possible predator, "attack me at your peril." Moreover, when first disturbed a skunk will go through an elaborate aggressive display, designed to bring these warning markings in the most effective way to the attention of the animal threatening it. These displays vary with different species.

The common striped skunk, *Mephitis mephitis*, raises its plumed tail over its back and stamps its feet threateningly on the ground. The little spotted skunk, *Spilogale putorius*, is even more emphatic. Doing a handstand, this species supports itself on its forelimbs, with its hind limbs raised vertically in the air so that the full extent of its spotted back is shown to the aggressor. It can maintain this attitude for five or six seconds at a time and it is a very rash or inexperienced predator that will not in such circumstances hastily decamp. If it fails to do so, the skunk will next discharge its anal glands with great precision in the direction of its foe. Although not fatal, the results are so demoralizing that the attacker, if intelligent, will tend in the future to give the conspicuous black-and-white markings a wide berth.

When the days are shorter, in October, another molt commences, and white hairs begin to replace the brown, working their way up the sides and spreading over the back, giving the animal a dappled appearance. By November it is all winter white except for the black tip of its tail. Weasels that live in warm climates also change their coats in fall, but the new fur comes in brown as before—not white.

As a final example of a physical defensive mechanism in mammals, a word must be said about self-amputation of the tail. This reaction to attack is, of course, very well known in many lizards which, if grasped by the tail or even if excited to extreme fear without being touched, will abandon part of it before dashing away into cover. The fact that certain mammals practice a similar defensive technique is not nearly so well known. Yet several small rodents, particularly dormice and field mice, are quite as capable of shedding part of their tails in emergency as lizards are, although the means by which this is achieved is somewhat different. Whereas the lizard tail drops away as a result of a clean break occurring in the middle of one of the vertebrae, a mouse only sheds part of the tissue in which its tail is encased. The tail is not thereby shortened, but a predator who grasps it is left only with its outer cover, while the mouse, with the inner part of the tail, escapes. Again in contrast to lizards, which can regenerate their tails at least partially, the denuded portion of the mouse's tail withers away in a few days and drops off. The value of this adaptation is suggested by the observations of field workers who have reported seeing more mice with mutilated than with intact tails.

Apart from the physical aspects of attack and defense, what are the patterns of behavior adopted by mammals to achieve their aggressive or defensive ends? The majority of these, as might be expected, are closely related to movement, although some species also find safety in cooperation and numbers. Musk oxen,

for example, if attacked by wolves, form a defensive circle, with the calves and young animals inside. Prairie dogs exhibit another type of defensive cooperation. Individuals sighting danger utter shrill cries which warn their neighbors to take cover. In similar circumstances a beaver will slap the water with its tail, signaling to the others in the colony that an enemy is approaching.

The most obvious method by which an individual animal can escape from a threatening predator is by running away. Flight is, indeed, the most common expedient adopted by those mammals which are the hunted rather than the hunter. Flight, however, is obviously useless if the pursuer can run faster than the pursued—unless by chance there is nearby cover which can be reached in time. Because of this, several mammals have adopted other techniques which either are used from the beginning or are substituted for flight when this proves to be useless.

What often happens is as follows. First, the predator begins to stalk its victim, which at this time may not be unduly disturbed. But when the distance between the two animals is narrowed to a certain point, the quarry is stimulated to flight. The predator must then decide either to dash directly after the quarry or allow time for its intended victim to settle down again so that it may make a new, and perhaps closer, approach. Even in the second case the moment comes when the predator must decide that it is the time to make a now-or-never attempt to reach its prey. Abandoning stealth, it rushes forward and the quarry dashes off at full speed.

But if the quarry realizes (although whether consciously or instinctively it would be difficult to say) that flight is useless, it often adopts a quite different behavior pattern. In a last desperate effort to save itself, it may turn to face its persecutor and place itself in an aggressive attitude. Sometimes this sudden change of technique so surprises the predator that it will be shocked into temporary confusion, allowing the quarry a new chance to escape. A rabbit will sometimes do this, at the last gasp turning on the pursuing hound. In a somewhat different but quite comparable context, the weak boy at school may, in desperation, suddenly face the bully who is tormenting him and by a lucky blow put the larger boy to flight.

ANOTHER rather special defensive technique utilized by mammals is sheer immobility. The rabbit or deer "freezes" in its tracks at the sight of an enemy and perhaps escapes detection. The habit of freezing is also used by predators, especially by members of the cat family stalking their prey. Anyone who has watched a domestic cat stalking a bird feeding on the ground will have observed how the cat advances in a series of short quick runs, pausing in between in a completely rigid attitude.

The classic example of the use of immobility as a survival technique is the death feigning of the American opossum, and the term "playing possum" has passed into general usage to describe such behavior. This animal, if attacked or frightened, sometimes falls down on its side in a position that most realistically resembles death. The withered-looking ears and bare tail are themselves suggestive of a corpse, and the opossum also draws back its lips to expose the teeth in a set grimace. The attacking animal, after a few sniffs at the prostrate body, will generally move away. A few minutes later, however, when the coast is clear, the "corpse" will come to life and assume its normal activities. This behavior, incidentally, is probably physiological, for the sham is almost certainly a shock reaction to a crisis situation.

PARTIALLY CONCEALED BY TALL GRASS, A LONE BENGAL TIGER WAITS IN AMBUSH NEAR TRACKS MADE BY ANTELOPE, DEER AND OTHER GAME

The Quick and the Dead

All of the survival devices developed by other animals have been adopted by mammals: various tactics of pursuit, group cooperation, and such weaponry as teeth and claws, spines, armor, scent and poison glands. Even the habit of feigning death is not unique. But mammals are more intelligent: many can quickly change their usual modes of attack and defense to cope with new circumstances.

Cooperative Hunting of the Pack

Hunting in groups is a particularly mammalian trait, depending on a high order of cooperation and intelligence. The wolves and their allies regularly run in packs and are able to bring down swift and resourceful, as well as larger and stronger, prey.

The relationship between wolves and moose has been studied in detail on Isle Royale in Lake Superior. In summer the wolves' favorite fare of moose is supplemented by beaver and small game, but with the coming of freeze-up these disappear, and the lone big moose is the prime target. The wolves range single file for miles until they sight one, then spread out downwind and stand still as pointers. Then they make a sudden rush, one large wolf heading for the quarry while the rest string out behind. If the moose runs, they close in, snapping at its rump and flanks. It may escape, but once a vital spot is hit, it dies in minutes. A moose that stands its ground, however, can always hold off the wolves until they slink away.

HELD OFF by a strong adult moose, wolves maneuver, trying to make their quarry turn and run. In this instance they attacked, but the kill seemed too difficult and they soon trotted off to seek weaker prey. Biologists studying Isle Royale wolves found that a large pack of 16 individuals trails and harasses about 12 moose for every one that is killed.

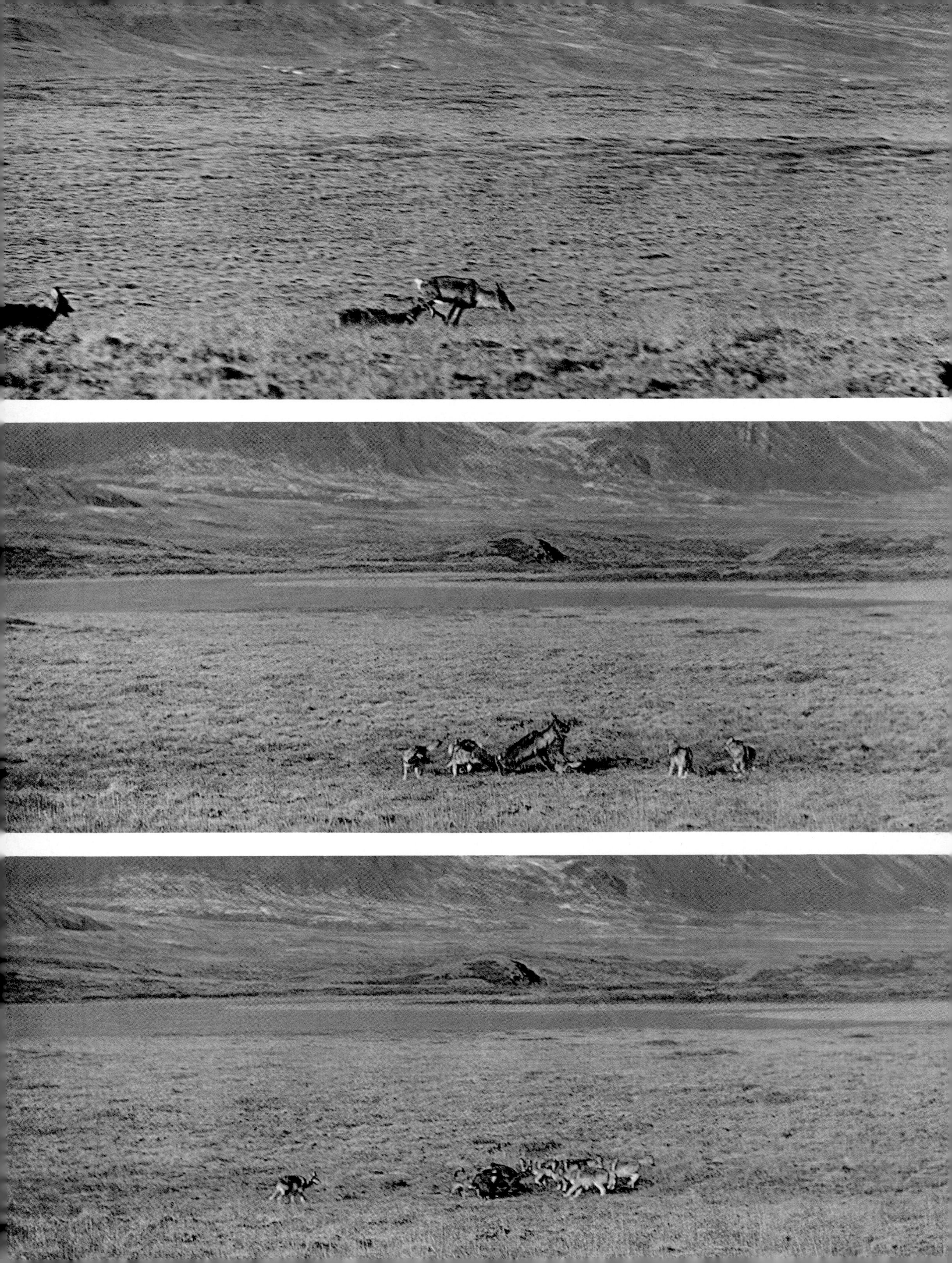

Learning to Cooperate with Other Mammals

The first lessons in self-sufficiency begin when the parent of a carnivore brings disabled but living prey—a small ground squirrel, mouse or rat—for the young to practice hunting and killing. The capture of larger food animals requires more patience and skill. Young wolves on the Alaskan tundra learn how to do this by accompanying and watching older members of the pack. When half-grown, they help in running down a caribou, but do not touch it until a more experienced wolf has made the kill. Later they will cooperate fully in stalking, attacking, killing and eating the prey. The learning process never stops, for every hunt poses some new problems. Occasionally a member of the dog or weasel family is so adaptable that it learns to travel and hunt with an individual of another species. This kind of association, based on self-interest, lasts as long as it is of some benefit to one or perhaps both of the partners.

A CARIBOU IS TAKEN by young wolves north of Brooks Range, Alaska. This animal, ill or injured, has tired and fallen behind the herd. The wolf pups' adopted leader, an Eskimo dog, is able to hamstring the animal *(top)* and bring it down by the throat *(center)*. After the dog begins to feed *(bottom)*, the wolves close in and share the kill.

A HARE IS CAUGHT by a coyote with the help of a badger, which flushes it from a brush pile. Hunting associations between these two animals occur in nature around prairie-dog towns. This one was developed by baiting an area until the animals learned to visit it together. The coyote benefited this time; another time the badger may.

AS THREE LIONS GET READY TO ATTACK SOME UNEASY WILDEBEEST, THE ONE AT RIGHT STARTS TO MANEUVER BEHIND AND UPWIND OF THEM.

The Strategy of Stalking

Unlike the members of the dog family, cats depend on stealth and the quick dash to secure their prey, and usually hunt alone or in pairs. Some exceptions are the Canada lynx, whose young accompany the mother through the first winter, and the lions on the African plains that travel in family groups, or "prides." Although they do not run as a pack, three or four members of the pride occasionally cooperate in hunting, and when they do, their strategy is deliberate and organized. An experienced lion generally moves upwind of a herd and, by growling and giving the uneasy animals its scent, causes them to

AMBUSH AT A RIVER BANK: WHILE ONE LIONESS STAMPEDES A HERD OF IMPALA, ANOTHER (BELOW) INTERCEPTS THE ANIMALS' FAST DASH FOR THE

ITS DRIFTING SCENT AND MENACING GRUNTS WILL THEN STAMPEDE THE HERD TOWARD THE WAITING PAIR, ONE OF WHICH WILL MAKE THE KILL

stampede toward the hunting party. A lioness usually makes the kill, but the old males eat first, followed by the females and young. The remains of the carcass ordinarily fall to hyenas, jackals and vultures.

When close enough, a lion simply stalks and then rushes at its quarry. If it can get within 30 yards of an antelope, it can usually pull it down in a few bounds. The maximum speed of the charge is about 35 miles an hour. However, a lion is not so well adapted for the chase as the lithe cheetah, which is capable of running down its victim at 65 to 70 miles an hour. It can maintain this pace for a quarter mile.

SAFETY OF THE BUSH. ALTHOUGH THE LEAD IMPALA ESCAPES BY LEAPING, ONE THAT IS FOLLOWING RUNS INTO THE LIONESS AND IS BROUGHT DOWN

CHASED BY A DOG, an opossum is soon overtaken *(above)*. It attempts to escape the bites of its attacker by rolling over "dead" *(opposite)*, with body still, eyes glassy and mouth agape. This may be shock or sham.

The Tactics of Bluff

When an animal cannot get away, it may try to appear larger and fiercer than it really is, it may fight back in desperation or even feign death. The smaller and weaker mammals display a variety of these defensive reactions. Certain shrews hump their backs, grate their teeth and utter high-pitched squeaks; then, as an ultimate gesture, they collapse on their backs with spread and waving feet, repeating staccato notes. Other rodents, such as the house mouse and the European field mouse, rear up, bite and spar silently with their front feet, and the ordinarily inoffensive cottontail rabbit has been known to kick

EVEN THE TIMID RABBIT SHOWS FIGHT WHEN CORNERED. THIS ONE WAS POSING FOR A NATURE PHOTOGRAPHER IN THE WOODS WHEN A RACCOON

APPARENTLY LIFELESS, the opossum discourages the dog, which leaves *(above)*. In a few minutes the animal recovers, changes position and looks around cautiously *(right)* before scrambling to its feet and running off.

a bobcat in the face with its strong hind legs. Although opossums may try to bluff larger animals by hissing and baring their teeth, they are the best of the pretenders among the higher animals. A pursuing dog can easily catch a running opossum and kill it, but if it "plays dead," it usually will not be molested. When it does this, the opossum may be pretending, or actually scared into a state of catalepsy, in which its heart rate slows down and it can stay motionless for a span of as little as eight seconds to as long as six hours. The jackal, honey badger and striped hyena may also faint or feign death.

WANDERED BY. THE STARTLED RABBIT, WITHOUT FURTHER ADO, LEAPED AT THE INTRUDER AND DROVE IT OFF WITH A FEW WELL-PLACED KICKS

TURNED ON ITS BACK, a hedgehog reveals its only vulnerable spot when rolled in a defensive ball. Right side up, it would present a prickly mouthful to a predator, with nose and toes tucked in and its loose spine-covered skin drawn as close around the soft under parts as possible. An occasional very hungry fox or badger learns the trick of turning a hedgehog over to kill it.

Sharp Quills and Hard-to-Crack Defenses

Some mammals combine special external protections with the ability to roll into a defensive ball, which makes their capture difficult or unrewarding. The pangolin and various armadillos, which are armored, all roll up. Porcupines, however, are often overtly aggressive. They advertise their presence loudly and, when irritated, erect their quills. A swat from a porcupine tail will embed hundreds of quills in a predator. The European hedgehog is also noisy in its movements, but it usually curls up when threatened. An active climber, it occasionally falls from heights, and its quills act as a cushion on landing.

ROLLED UP TIGHT, a three-banded armadillo is almost invulnerable. It has tough, arched shields covering each end of its body, and these are connected by three bony rings which, acting like the joints in medieval armor, give the animal the flexibility needed to curl up. The long triangular head and the smaller tail are also armored and fit snugly to complete the protection.

PROTECTIVE CAMOUFLAGE helps hide most young and adult mammals from predators that hunt by sight as well as by smell and hearing. Most mammals are color-blind and would see this fawn as it appears in monochrome at left, not as it would look to those primates, birds and reptiles that do have color vision. The spotted coat on the fawn of the white-tailed deer duplicates

the dappling of light and shadow filtering through the foliage. As long as the animal does not move, it blends into its surroundings. It also lacks body scent that might attract predators. Many of the cats are similarly spotted or striped, enabling them to crouch unnoticed while hunting. Such color schemes do not depend on hue, but gain their effectiveness from tones and patterns.

AT THE START OF THE FIGHT, a mongoose threatens an Indian cobra by displaying its teeth. The snake counters by opening its mouth wide, spreading its hood and rearing back, ready to strike.

THE COBRA STRIKES, but its fast-moving opponent jumps out of reach, weaving and rocking on its feet like a boxer waiting for an opening. The snake retracts, strikes, misses again and again.

WHEN THE SNAKE HAS TIRED from repeated striking, the mongoose leaps up and pounces. A cobra can often withstand the first bite and shake the animal off, but the mongoose persists.

"This Shall End When One Is Dead"

Encounters between two animals that are both well equipped to fight also occur in nature, and when they do there may be a prolonged struggle to the death. The Indian mongoose has, through many centuries, earned the reputation of a snake killer. Its prowess is celebrated in a jungle story by Rudyard Kipling in which a pet mongoose, Rikki-Tikki-Tavi, battles and kills a pair of cobras that attack him in defense of their nest. It is not true, however, that "all a grown mongoose's business in life is to fight and kill snakes." It preys on nearly anything it can get, including grasshoppers, frogs, lizards, nesting birds, rats and some of the smaller snakes, rarely attacking large poisonous snakes. But when mongoose and cobra, for whatever reason, become engaged at close quarters, there is no escape for either. The fatal dance must go on, snake's blow against mongoose's jump for an hour or more. The cobra usually loses because it cannot strike or retract fast enough and is not adapted to stab, but must bite to inject venom. In a fight with a constrictor or a pit viper, the mammal would be at a disadvantage.

THE FIGHT ENDS WHEN THE MONGOOSE IS ABLE TO HOLD AND CRACK THE COBRA'S SKULL

MIGRATING AT SEA away from their breeding grounds in the Aleutians, a small flotilla of Steller sea lions churns north. In summer, they may wander as far as St. Lawrence Island before returning southward again.

6

The Wanderers and the Stay-at-Homes

DIFFERENT individuals of our own species are, as we know, sometimes stay-at-homes and sometimes wanderers. In the old village societies of Europe it is still quite common to find peasants who, during the whole of their lives, have never been more than a dozen miles from their birthplace. By contrast there are others who thrive on movement and adventure. They would feel as cramped and unhappy in a local community as would a simple villager if he were thrown into the life of a big city.

In the world of mammals, species are to be found that correspond quite closely to both these types of humans. Sedentary mammals are usually those that have a good local food supply and a congenial climate and thus have no strong stimulus to movement. Wandering mammals, by contrast, may be prompted to travel by seasonal shortages of food, local overpopulation, a need to avoid severe weather at certain times of year and so on. The comparison with humans is obvious in both cases. In fact, the only type of stimulus to movement found in man which does not seem to occur in any other mammal is the scientific or poetic curiosity, or simply the desire to conquer some challenge, which drives adventurous people to journey to the poles or the peaks of high mountains—

either in pursuit of knowledge or for pride of achievement without expectation of material gain.

Of the actual homes constructed by mammals the most common and typical is the burrow. Characteristic of smaller species, it varies in design from a simple hole in the ground to an elaborate network of subterranean tunnels. Mammals as different as the platypus and the red fox, the rabbit and the armadillo, all construct burrows. One of the most efficient mammalian burrowers is the European mole, which spends the greater part of its life underground and comes to the surface only occasionally. The burrows dug out by moles are often of remarkable complexity. Beneath the familiar molehill rising above the surface of the ground, there is an oval chamber, or nest, lined with dead grass and leaves. From the floor of the nest a tunnel usually slants downward, leading away from the nest and then to a surface exit for quick escape in case of danger. On marshy ground, this tunnel may be vertical and used for drainage. Permanent galleries lead off from the sides of the nest and may extend for many yards in any direction, providing routes to the mole's subterranean hunting grounds. At their extremities or at various places along their length, the mole burrows off through the soil in search of the earthworms that are its main food. It thus forms temporary hunting galleries which are constantly being reconstructed as the mole burrows in new directions, the surplus earth being thrown out on the surface to form the small mounds which cluster round the main molehill. Moles can dig very fast indeed, and one species, the North American common, or eastern, mole, has been estimated to burrow at a rate of some 12 feet an hour.

One of the most complex burrows is that made by the European badger. The primary burrow of this species may consist of a fairly short tunnel with a terminal nest, but as badgers habitually associate in large family groups, this simple structure develops into a labyrinth as generation follows generation. The original nest forms the starting point for new burrows terminating in new chambers which serve as dormitories and retreats for breeding females. As the whole structure increases in complexity, new exits are made from the primary burrow, relieving the congestion and also allowing the inmates alternative means of escape in case of emergency.

The use of burrows is not always communal, and sometimes even the male and female of a breeding pair will have separate homes. Different burrows may

also be occupied at different times of year or be specialized for sleeping, breeding and storage. For instance, the three-toed jerboa of Asia uses both temporary and permanent summer burrows. The temporary one consists only of a simple tunnel, but the permanent burrow is a complicated structure with a main entrance, which is blocked up with sand in the daytime, several emergency exits, a bed chamber and a narrow passage deep in the ground to which the jerboa retires during the hottest hours of the day. Each sex has its own summer burrow, the male's being simpler than the female's. Moreover, the animals construct special winter burrows which lie deeper in the ground.

MANY mammals retire to their underground burrows in the fall or early winter and sleep through the cold months. Bears, skunks and opossums, among others, lapse into prolonged but fairly normal slumber, for they wake up from time to time and move about. But others—woodchucks, jumping mice and ground squirrels, for example—are true hibernators. When a ground squirrel hibernates, its body temperature sometimes drops to only a few degrees above freezing. From a normal 200 to 400 beats per minute its heart may slow to five, and its breathing from nearly 200 respirations per minute to four or less. Hibernating woodchucks that breathed only once every five minutes have been observed. Curled up in a tight ball, its bodily functions drastically slowed down, the hibernating animal appears to be dead.

The physiological stimuli that trigger hibernation are not yet fully understood, but the process often, yet not always, coincides with the coming of cold weather or lack of food. Woodchucks retire to their dens, very fat, in late September or October, when the weather is still mild and plenty of green food is still growing all about them, and sleep for six months or more. The Columbian ground squirrel sleeps even longer, for it retires to its burrow in July, at the hottest and driest time of the year.

Apart from the burrowers, a number of mammals construct permanent or temporary homes and sheltering places aboveground. These are usually very rudimentary compared with the elaborate nests made by birds, but some are quite ambitious. The beaver, famous for its dams and lodges, is one of the most notable mammalian architects, but the muskrat also shows considerable building skill. These rodents sometimes live in burrows in the banks of rivers and lakes in their native North America, as well as in Europe, where they were intro-

THE SNUG WORLD OF THE BEAVER

Like a small domed fortress, a beaver lodge rises from the pond formed by a dam. It is constructed of branches and the trunks of saplings plastered with mud, has an air hole in the ceiling and contains a single chamber about five feet wide and three feet high. An underwater exit leads outside, and close by stands a stockpile of branches, whose bark the beavers will eat during the coldest parts of winter, when frozen sap makes trees too hard to cut down. Beavers repair and add to their lodge as long as it is occupied, and must also do steady maintenance work on their dam.

duced in 1905. But apart from their burrows, they also construct houses somewhat reminiscent of beaver lodges in marshes or along the banks of streams.

Among more temporary structures, the nests of harvest mice, both European and American, show a considerable degree of constructional skill. These little animals are usually found in open country, particularly in fields of high grasses. The nest is a ball-shaped tangle of grass strands and may be anywhere from six inches to several feet above the ground. It is often at least partly composed of the leaves of the grass on which it hangs, and these may continue to grow while the nest is occupied. The mice can run with great agility up and down the stems of the grasses, using their tails, which they coil around the stems, as additional grasping organs.

The naturalist Elden H. Vestal has described another particularly remarkable type of shelter, the home built by the dusky-footed wood rat of western North America. These nests, which are occupied only by a single individual, are often conical structures built round a tree trunk, although they are also found on branches and rocky ledges. Made of twigs, leaves and dead plants, they are often of remarkable size, a height of four feet being quite usual. Their owners repair them constantly and keep them in good condition. A tunnel leads from the outside world to the main living quarters, and further tunnels connect this with a sanitary chamber and perhaps a secondary chamber. In desert areas, wood rats sometimes build their homes in the midst of clumps of cactus and then barricade the nest and its approaches with the cactus spines.

NONHUMAN primates do not make such elaborate homes as their advanced brains might lead us to expect. Even anthropoids such as gorillas, orangutans and chimpanzees limit their building activities to constructing rough nests of branches, either on the ground or in trees, on which they may sleep for just one night. Several species of bats, on the other hand, use some very interesting temporary shelters. Thus some Old World forms will sleep in banana leaves, porcupine burrows and even inside bamboo stems. Two tropical American species actually fashion shelters for themselves out of the leaves of palm trees, cutting them with their teeth so that they sag to form a concealing tent.

Hoofed mammals do not normally have fixed homes. These animals, all of which are the quarry of predators, can only survive by constant movement, and to have a local headquarters where their foes knew they could be found at certain times would be fatal to them. However, when the breeding season approaches, the females of some hoofed mammals do seek out a temporary resting place where they can give birth to their young. Thus in several species of deer and antelopes, the pregnant female will withdraw to a sheltered spot such as a thicket or an out-of-the-way ledge on a hillside shortly before delivery. Even so large an animal as the elephant will retire in this way, and the expectant mother is usually accompanied by another female from the herd, a kind of "aunt," who helps protect the newborn calf. Such temporary quarters are not prepared or furnished in any way; they are merely retreats occupied for very limited periods by animals that are usually on the move.

A similar situation occurs among marine mammals, for their aquatic environment makes them all, to a greater or lesser extent, wanderers. The beaches which form the breeding grounds of seals and their allies might be termed homes of a kind, but they are not prepared in any way and are only occupied at certain seasons. When swimming at large in the open sea, marine mammals do not make any one place their permanent center. However, some of them do have sleeping habits of a rather special kind. Thus the sea otter will lie on its back to sleep, clinging to large clumps of seaweed with its forepaws or wrapping strands around its body to avoid drifting.

We can see now that the mammalian "home" has three main uses: it is a place to sleep, a place to breed and raise young, and a defensive citadel. Sometimes, as in burrows, it fulfills all three functions. But even the most elaborate home made by subhuman mammals is a very simple affair compared with that made by the most primitive members of our own species. This is because one of the differences which distinguishes man from his fellow mammals is that he habitually acquires possessions and needs a base in which they can be stored.

ALTHOUGH a home in the human sense is not a high priority for mammals, many species are extremely restricted in range and will make extraordinary efforts to return to their birthplace if for some reason they are removed from it. The local area in which a mammal operates is known as its home range; this is the region where it knows every landmark and hiding place and in which it can most efficiently obtain food and defend itself from predators. The home range of a small mammal may be very restricted. Experiments made by recapturing previously marked brown rats have shown that the great majority had moved no more than 40 feet from the place where they were marked. Desert species may range more widely than this because they need to cover more ground in search of food, but on the whole, small mammals habitually remain within a few hundred yards of their birthplace unless there is some very strong stimulus to wider movement. In large species the range is proportionately increased. The European brown bear and the American grizzly are known to wander across an area some 12 miles in diameter. Herbivores and such active predators as wolves often have a far larger range, and movements of up to 30 miles in any one direction are not uncommon.

Quite apart from local movements over a more or less restricted territory, certain mammals make far longer journeys each year, sometimes covering hundreds of miles. The main object of these seasonal migrations seems to be to combine the advantage of an abundance of lush food when the young are born with that of a cozy retreat in the winter. Apart from such true migrations, the search for favorite foods may lead to a certain amount of nomadism among mammals. However, neither true migration nor nomadism should be confused with the simple extension of range which can often be observed in active and successful species, or with the "emigrations" of such mammals as the lemming, which will be dealt with later in this chapter.

Examples of true migrations can be found among many types of mammals, but the large hoofed mammals have a particularly spectacular range. For instance, the caribou of North America may travel between 400 and 500 miles on its seasonal journeys. The wandering propensities of this animal have been known to naturalists for hundreds of years, and detailed work on the subject has been carried out for at least a century. It was found that during the summer the caribou live in the tundra regions north of the timber line, but from July onward they begin a generally southward movement along regular routes which seem to be followed year after year. It is on this journey that breeding takes place. The caribou remain in their winter quarters until the following spring, when the northward movement begins again, the young being born during the course of the journey. The caribou press on despite all obstacles, and mass drownings sometimes occur when they attempt to cross swollen streams. C.H.D. Clarke, who has made extensive observations, mentions an occasion when over 500 of them were drowned at one time.

Sea and air provide less obvious barriers to travel than land for the mammals that inhabit them, so it is not surprising that migration is particularly common in these environments. The great blue whale, the largest mammal of all time, is one sea creature that makes spectacular journeys. There are records of a blue whale having traveled 300 miles in 32 days and of another which traveled 500 miles in 88 days. Such data are obtained by marking whales with stainless steel cartridges that can be fired from a gun and embed themselves in the animal's blubber. If, at some future time, the whale is caught, the cartridge can be extracted and referred to a central authority which keeps a record of the place where the animal was marked. Marathon journeys of over 1,000 miles have been recorded for blue whales, although these do not appear to be usual.

The movement of gray whales along the coast of southern California during the winter months is also well known. This species bears its young in sheltered lagoons along the coast of Baja California during this time and then starts to move northward along the coast with the approach of warm weather. By summer these whales are patrolling the north Pacific and Arctic Oceans, feeding on the abundant supplies of plankton which they find there at this time.

Other whales well known for their seasonal migrations are the humpbacks. In the southern winter these mammals breed in the tropical seas along the coasts of South America, Africa, New Zealand and Australia, but during the southern summer, from November to April, they are found along the northern shores of the antarctic continent. These seasonal migrations cause the humpback whale to move regularly through at least 40 degrees of latitude. The fin whale is also a great traveler between antarctic and tropical waters, and records exist of at least one specimen being found nearly 2,000 miles from the place where it was originally tagged.

MIGRATION ROUTE
OF THE ALASKAN FUR SEAL

Male and female Alaskan fur seals spend their winters far apart, but gather each summer at the Pribilof Islands to breed. The adult males, having wintered not far away in the Gulf of Alaska, arrive alone early in June to stake out territories on the beach. A few weeks later the females arrive after a journey of some 3,000 miles from their winter quarters off the coast of California. Pups are born in June, but learn to swim so quickly that by autumn they can join the migration south.

BATS also often migrate over long distances. Journeys made by these animals are not as long as those made by marine mammals, nor by birds, but they nevertheless often cover many hundreds of miles. The tiny European pipistrelle, for example, travels regularly between southeastern Europe and the central provinces of Russia, a distance of some 600 to 800 miles. The Mexican free-tail bats that live during the summer months in the southern United States travel an equal distance. Several of these have been found to migrate from Tucson, Arizona, to Jalisco, Mexico.

In the study of bat movements, individuals are banded on the forelimbs with metal rings and, as with whales, recoveries are reported to a central authority. The proportion of recoveries is not large, being rather less than three in every 100 bats marked, but it is enough to show there is a constant migratory pattern and distances of 100 miles or more are covered in three to four weeks.

Is it possible to say whether or not these journeys are consciously decided upon? Can we believe that, at a certain time of the year, a bat or whale or caribou thinks to itself, as a man might: "Well, conditions are getting pretty uncongenial here, it's time I took off for foreign parts." The answer is certainly No. The urge to migrate, like so many other aspects of animal behavior, is based on physiological stimuli. Glandular secretions and other physical transformations in the animal's body operating in a seasonal rhythm are mainly responsible for dictating what it will do.

Another question that must inevitably be asked concerning migratory mammals is: "How do they find their way?" Before attempting an answer, it is necessary to give a few instances of homing by mammals which have been proved by scientific experiment. François Bourlière, in his classic work *The Natural History of Mammals*, has quoted several of these, especially some outstanding results that have been achieved with rodents and bats. Thus deer mice, which normally have a home range of only about 100 yards in diameter, have been known to come back to their base from a distance of two miles within 48 hours after artificial displacement. The homing of bats seems to be even more remarkable, and noctules have returned to their home range from a point 28 miles away in 24 hours. Over longer periods, there are well-authenticated reports of still greater distances being covered by bats, the maximum being 165 miles. These instances must be considered in relation to the capacity for orientation observed in certain domestic animals, particularly dogs and cats, which have often been known to find their way home from places between 10 and 25 miles away, and sometimes even more.

In attempting to explain how such movements are achieved, it is certainly essential first to consider the hypotheses based upon common sense. For example, a dog that was taken 20 miles from home by rail is known to have made its way back by following the railroad track until it reached familiar territory. An element of luck must also be allowed for, and it seems probable that setting out in chance directions until a familiar landmark is sighted may account for some of the recorded cases of successful homing. But such explanations do not adequately account for all such cases and certainly not the mass seasonal movements described earlier in this chapter.

Experiments made with birds may throw some light on the matter. It now appears likely that migratory birds rely to a considerable extent on the stars as navigation aids in making long journeys, and celestial navigation may likewise play a part in the direction finding of mammals, especially in the migrations of bats. The aid given by long-established trails and the transmission of a knowledge of landmarks from one generation to the next must also be taken into account. Yet even when such factors have been allowed for, it must be admitted that a large core of mystery still remains. It seems reasonable to assume that a direction-finding instinct is part of the inbuilt genetic equipment of migratory mammals. The time has not yet come, however, when the laws governing its operation are fully understood.

There is another type of mammalian movement which can be defined quite simply as emigration. The difference between emigration and migration is that whereas migratory mammals return to where they came from the following season, emigrants leave their homeland and do not return. The reasons why emigration occurs are quite complex, but basically it seems to result from increasing competition in the original habitat. As it becomes harder and harder to obtain a living in a certain region, owing to population pressure, shortage of suitable foods or the presence of more efficient competitors, animals tend to move away from their homelands into new regions.

Thus, from colonial times, mass emigrations of gray squirrels have frequently been noted in North America. Audubon and Bachman, in their famous work *The Quadrupeds of North America*, recorded this tendency in the squirrels of the eastern United States and erroneously gave them the name *Sciurus migratorius* because of it. Describing the mass movements of this species, they wrote: "Onward they come, devouring on their way every thing that is suited to their

MIGRATION ROUTE OF THE HUMPBACK WHALE

A slow but steady traveler, the humpback whale may swim as far as 4,000 miles at speeds that average 4.3 knots during its regular seasonal migrations. All through the warm southern summer it has done little but gorge on the krill that abound in antarctic waters. In May it moves north to warmer tropical seas, where it breeds and calves but does not eat. Because it frequents shallow coastal waters, the habits of the humpback are better known than those of many larger baleen whales.

taste, laying waste corn and wheat-fields of the farmer." One of the greatest of these treks occurred in 1842 in Wisconsin and lasted for four weeks. Basing his figures on the number of squirrels that passed a given point every hour as described by an eyewitness, Ernest Thompson Seton estimated—perhaps with exaggeration, that about 450 million squirrels took part in this movement. Whatever the real figure, vast numbers of squirrels were certainly involved. William J. Hamilton Jr. describes more recent emigrations in Connecticut and New York in the 1930s, when thousands of squirrels were killed on the highways or drowned while crossing the Connecticut River.

An increase of range following the stimulus of environmental pressure may be a very good thing, and colonization of new regions is important in evolution and important to the success of the species. Mammals as different as mice and men have demonstrated how very uncongenial regions of the earth's surface can be exploited to support life. Sometimes, however, enforced emigration due to unresolved biological pressures at home may have disastrous consequences. An example of this which has always captured the imagination of scientists and laymen alike is the emigration of the Norwegian lemmings.

These small, largely nocturnal rodents inhabit the plateaus and mountain slopes of the Scandinavian peninsula. For years at a time they may be extremely rare in the region, but periodically an astonishing increase in their fecundity causes them to swarm in immense numbers. The periods when this occurs have been systematically recorded by naturalists and are known as lemming years. The causes of the swarming are still not completely understood, but one explanation is this. At certain times a group of lemmings is favored by an exceptional abundance of food. The first result is a very rapid increase in the frequency and size of their litters. As these favorable conditions continue over several years, an enormous expansion of the population takes place. But however abundant the food supply, a point is eventually reached every three or four years where the carrying capacity of the habitat is exceeded and a mass emigration of the surplus population occurs.

THIS emigration is spectacular. As congestion increases in their overcrowded homes, thousands, and indeed millions, of lemmings set forth in pursuit of better conditions. Contrary to popular belief, they do not normally travel at first in large bands, but one by one. However, when some natural barrier such as a river is encountered, the procession of lemmings will pile up until vast agglomerations occur. Eventually a mass movement into the water begins, and many thousands of lemmings are drowned in attempting the crossing. The last act in the drama occurs when the survivors reach the sea. Here a great concentration of animals gradually builds up on the shore until the pressure becomes so great that they begin to throw themselves into the water. The naturalist Walter Heape has quoted an instance of a vessel steaming in a fiord which passed for a quarter of an hour through a shoal of emigrant lemmings. The shoal, he says, was at least two or three miles wide, and the number of swimmers had to be reckoned in millions. Moreover, it formed only a single branch of a far greater horde whose size it was impossible to estimate. Except for a few individuals that may be lucky enough to land on an offshore island in the course of such emigrations, there is, of course, no hope at all that any of the animals will ever make a landfall; all are drowned. Although the laws governing these suicidal emigrations by lemmings are now better understood, they still represent one of the most poignant and thought-provoking phenomena in nature.

A CARIBOU BULL, PERPETUALLY ON THE MOVE IN SEARCH OF LICHENS AND SHRUBS, MIGRATES ACROSS THE ALASKA TUNDRA IN AUTUMN

Comings and Goings

Although mammals as a group cannot match the mobility of birds, many of them travel great distances every year. Mountain lions are known to patrol ranges of 30 to 50 miles, and some of the large herbivores regularly migrate for hundreds of miles. However, many of the smaller mammals are remarkably sedentary and may stay within a few yards of their birthplaces throughout their lives.

The Migrators

The endless search for food or a safe place to rear their young encourages certain mammals—notably the large hoofed species—to make seasonal migrations. In western North America, bighorn sheep, mule deer and elk habitually pass their summers feeding on higher levels of the mountains. When the winter cold sets in, they move to the relatively protected valleys, where the snow is less deep and the food more accessible.

Migratory animals often travel in immense herds. On the Serengeti Plains of East Africa, where herds must escape drought rather than cold and snow, wildebeest by the thousands begin a 200-mile journey westward to the area around Lake Victoria when the dry season starts in June or July. In December, when the rainy season revives the parched grasslands, the vast assemblage makes the return journey.

Besides hoofed animals on land, other species migrate too. In the air, the gray-headed bats of Australia follow the seasonal ripening of the fruits on which they live. At sea, many aquatic mammals—particularly seals and some whales—go to the same places each year to breed.

FORDING A RIVER BAR IN ALASKA, a herd of caribou drifts toward summer grazing. Now dwindled from the millions that once made the trip, herds of several thousands still travel day and night along the same routes each year between their summer and winter feeding grounds.

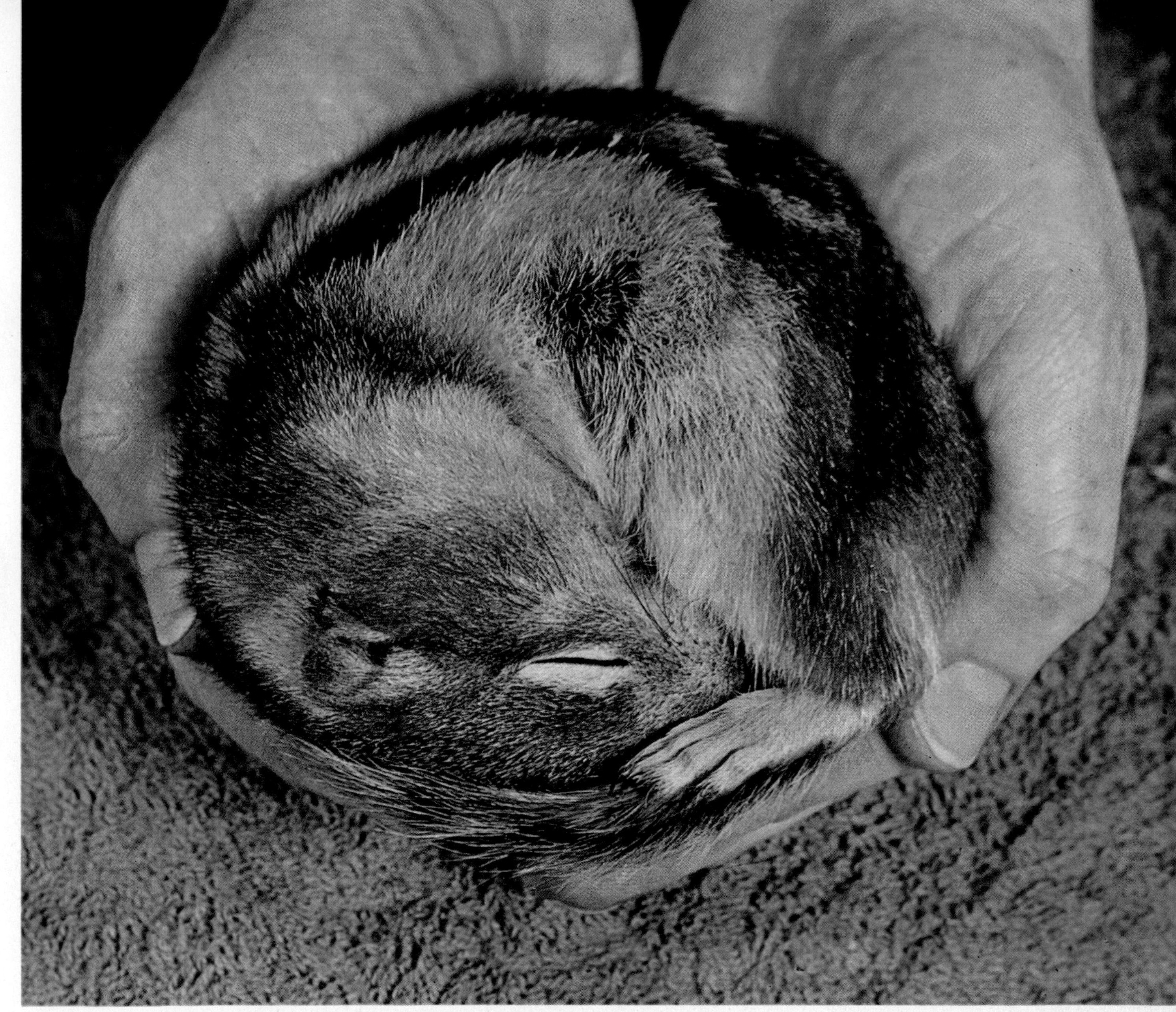
CURLED IN DEEP TORPOR, A FAMILIAR POSITION IN HIBERNATING ANIMALS, A GROUND SQUIRREL IS NOT EVEN DISTURBED WHEN HANDLED

Animals That Sleep through Seasons

Mammals that do not migrate or are unable to remain active when temperatures drop and the food supply dwindles pass these uncomfortable months in a state of torpor. Species like hedgehogs and dormice, which enter a true deep sleep during winter, undergo profound physiological changes to make their long fast possible. Their body temperatures sink to near freezing. Blood pressure falls, heartbeat drops to a few beats a minute and breathing becomes slow and irregular. Many endocrine glands almost cease to function for the duration of the torpor. Throughout the lethargy, fat which was accumulated earlier is slowly burned to supply the animal with the little energy it needs to sustain itself.

How long the sleep lasts usually depends on the temperature outside—the longer the cold, the longer the hibernation. In any case, it takes an animal hours to emerge from it upon waking in the spring.

HANGING BY ITS FEET inside a cave, a pipistrelle bat of North America is in a torpor that may last seven months. The glistening is caused by reflections from condensed moisture on its fur.

The Homemakers

Among mammals, the practice of building homes is limited to species that live alone or in single-family groups. The shelters they use may be as simple as the dry banana leaf in which the tropical opossum curls up for a night, or as complex as the prairie-dog towns that still may be found on the Great Plains of the American West.

One purpose of a home is to provide an animal with a safe place to live. Thus monkeys of tropical Africa often construct shelters of branches high in the trees, well out of the way of ground-dwelling predators. Other animals go underground. The desert gerbil does its digging more to escape the devastating heat of midday than to flee its enemies. Its underground home is sometimes as much as 30° cooler than the air outside.

Rodents are probably the most accomplished of mammal architects and they frequently build durable nests above ground to shelter their young. But not all homes are permanent places to which the animal returns over and over again. Gorillas construct new shelters every day. These are located in trees for females and young. But adult males, being too heavy to do much climbing, build crude nests on the ground with leaves and branches found nearby.

ON THE LOOKOUT, a weasel emerges from a hollow tree. Slim and supple, weasels can live in any narrow hole, and even take over mole or mouse nests, lining them with their victims' fur.

WEAVING A NEST, a harvest mouse works with its feet and teeth. Made of grass, these nests are attached to tall reeds. Inside, they are lined with milkweed floss and other soft materials.

CLEARING ITS BURROW, a hoary marmot carries a stone in its mouth. It will probably reline its nest with dried grasses, a common practice among these mountain-dwelling rodents.

DIGGING FURIOUSLY in the dry earth a prairie dog kicks up dirt with its hind feet. Its vertical shaft goes down for three or more feet and branches out to several separate living chambers.

A BEAVER'S SKULL shows the heavy, curved incisors set deep in the jaw, making them strong, powerful tools. The upper teeth are used for leverage; the lower ones for gnawing.

A VIEW OF A BEAVER POND SHOWS THE DAM, THE LODGE

A Skillful Engineer

Aside from man, the beaver is the most accomplished builder among the mammals. It makes dams and lodges, deepens pools, and digs elaborate canals and tunnels—all of this to create for itself living conditions that will secure it from predators. The key to it all is the dam; it backs up water to form a shallow pond in which a lodge can be built in a safe spot away from shore, easy for the strong-swimming beaver to reach but inaccessible to marauders.

GNAWING AT A TREE, a beaver eats the bark from the chips before discarding them. An extremely speedy worker, it can bring down a four-inch-thick poplar or aspen in less than 15 minutes.

CARRYING A BRANCH it has stripped from a felled tree, a beaver heads for its lodge or dam site. Later, it will cut up the trunk into sections small enough to be floated through the canals.

(LEFT CENTER) AND A CACHE OF FOOD BRANCHES (RIGHT CENTER). BEAVERS WORK MOSTLY AT NIGHT AND ARE SELDOM SEEN DURING THE DAY

REPAIRING THE DAM, a beaver lifts a branch from the pond after swimming with it through the water. It will pile the stick on the others it has collected. Dam repairs are made the year round.

A DEAD BEAVER lies under a tree it felled but failed to avoid. Such accidents are rare; the animal usually moves aside. The belief that beavers can fell trees in a desired direction is false.

A SWIMMING LESSON near a waterfall is given to two young beavers by their mother. Baby beavers leave their lodge for the first time and begin to swim when they are only a month old.

How the Beaver Builds

A beaver's construction work usually starts with the damming of a small stream with sticks, stones, grass and mud to create a pond six or eight feet deep. It first uses the materials closest at hand, and as they are consumed, the spreading waters of the pond bring other trees and bushes within easy reach. Ultimately, however, the pond reaches its full size, and the beavers in the colony have to go farther and farther afield. To do this they dig canals—sometimes hundreds of feet long and spanning many generations in the life of the colony. These are the highways along which sections of distant trees are brought to the pond for building dam and lodge and for food.

INSIDE THE LODGE, here opened to show its interior, three babies stay close to each other for warmth. The youngster at right has already learned to feed itself and is eating a strip of bark.

THE BEAVER'S TAIL, covered with tough scales, is used to propel and steer the animal through the water; as a brace when gnawing a tree; and to slap the water when danger threatens.

TENDER NUZZLING, like that at left, is characteristic of giraffes, which frequently rub their heads and necks together affectionately. During the courtship females adopt a swinging gait quite irresistible to the males.

7

Love Life

In the previous chapters we have mainly been looking at the way mammals go about such general activities as moving, eating, killing their prey and defending themselves from aggressors. This has meant thinking very largely of the various mammals as individuals—the way their bodies are made, what color and shape they are and how these things help them in the struggle for existence. But it is now time to discuss a topic of even greater interest, namely, how individual mammals interact with other members of their own species. This involves not only the basic sexual relationship between male and female, but also the ways in which mammals of both sexes behave in family groups and in the still more complex assemblages represented by mammalian societies.

Sexual reproduction is not universal in nature, and many very simple organisms, such as the one-celled protozoa, increase their numbers by simply dividing in two. As we go higher in the scale of life, however, the specializations of animals into male and female forms make the reproductive process a much more complicated business. They also offer a much higher potential for evolutionary advance, since the way organisms change is no longer dependent simply on mutations in an essentially isolated line. The development of new individuals from the germ cells of two parents allows a recombination of genes to occur in each successive generation, and natural selection can therefore operate upon a much wider range of individual variations.

The first preliminary to sexual union must, of course, be the selection of a mate, and in this, purely biological urges are usually decisive. The primary stimulus to copulation in most mammals is the physical condition of the female, who at certain times comes into the condition known as oestrus, or "heat." This word is derived from the Greek name for the gadfly, or warble fly, which was alleged to drive cattle mad. It is the time when the eggs are shed from the ovary and coincides with the production by the female of certain olfactory and behavioral stimuli that have an irresistible attraction for the male.

With some species oestrous cycles occur at regular intervals throughout the year. This is true not only of many primates, but also of representatives of such widely differentiated groups as bats, cats, whales and squirrels, to name a few. With a great number of other species, oestrus occurs only during certain "breeding seasons." Among some of the rodents, for example, there are repeated periods of heat during each breeding season and this arrangement enables a female quickly to have another chance to conceive if she has failed to do so during her first oestrous cycle. In contrast, many of the seals and weasels have just one period of heat a year. With the Alaskan fur seal and the fisher this occurs within a very few days after the birth of the young.

In many mammals the male gonads—the organs that produce the sex cells—are particularly active at certain seasons and the animal's desires become correspondingly aroused. In such mammals as deer and certain rodents, for instance, there is a definite season of male sexual excitement, or "rut," which corresponds with the period of female oestrus. This is particularly the case with mammals living in cold or temperate climates, where the breeding season is often closely correlated with the seasonal changes of the year. Thus the time of greatest awkwardness and heaviness for a female about to bear her young will tend to coincide with a period of greater abundance of easily obtainable food. The young are also born during this same period (usually spring), giving both mother and young a greater chance for survival during this time of potential danger for both. Among tropical species this correlation is much less marked; in the easier climatic conditions under which they live there tends to be less difference in the availability of food from season to season and breeding often continues throughout the year.

SECONDARY SEX CHARACTERISTICS

Differences in color, size, odor and other secondary features distinguish male from female in many species. The shoulder cape that adorns the male hamadryas baboon (left) is a conspicuous sexual identification. So too is the color of the hairless hindquarters, which are bright red in the male and pale pink in the smaller female.

Apart from such primary external differences between mammals of different sexes as the structure of the sex organs, many mammals possess secondary sex characteristics which are often of great importance in mating behavior. The manes of male lions and some species of male baboons, the antlers of deer, the inflatable proboscis of the male elephant seal, the facial hair of men and the rounded breasts of women are some of the more common examples of physical attributes which, in certain circumstances, have a powerful sexual significance in addition to any other function they may serve. Color may also be an important secondary sex character. This is less apparent in mammals than in birds, but is nevertheless very obvious in the males of such primate species as the mandrill, whose masklike face and multicolored hindquarters certainly play a part in sexual recognition and attraction.

In a good number of species, the two sexes have coats of different colors. There is a species of howling monkeys in which the males are black, while the females are usually a dingy yellowish color. In the great red kangaroo only the male is red; the female is blue-gray. The mature males of some antelopes also have colors and markings that differ from those of their mates and their young.

Sexual differences in size, too, are often striking, especially in the larger mammals. Fur seal bulls may weigh 600 pounds, while mature females average 75 pounds, and there is also a great disparity in size between the sexes in the sea lion and the elephant seal. Males of weasels and minks also may weigh twice as much as their mates.

A particularly important part is played in sexual union in mammals by the stimuli which act on the senses of touch and smell. When she is in heat, the female gives off a characteristic scent which is secreted from various glands and is often passed with her urine. This distinctive odor helps the male to locate his prospective mate and also stimulates his desire. For mating to occur at all it is necessary for both partners to be excited to the point where copulation is mechanically possible. The way in which this is achieved varies with different species, but kisses and caresses certainly play an important part in the love play of many lower mammals, just as they do in man. The effect of all these stimuli is also heightened in some species by a combination of sound and movement in a ritualistic display.

The male hooded seal, though only a couple of feet longer than the female, is about twice as heavy. But its most characteristic feature is the inflatable nose sac that it develops at puberty. This bladderlike sac is blown up to full size when the seal is angry at other males—which, during the mating season, is most of the time.

SEXUAL displays by mammals are generally less spectacular than those performed by birds, but they may nevertheless be quite elaborate. The male platypus, for example, courts his mate in the water, the two animals swimming in a tight circle, beak to tail. The male often grasps the female's tail in his beak and she "barrel rolls," turning over and over to twist free. There is also a great deal of mutual nuzzling and preening. Various rodents and other small mammals engage in rough-and-tumble "fights" or pursuits of one another during courtship and many engage in rigidly stylized movements. Francois Bourlière has described how the male hedgehog will circle round his mate for hours, puffing and blowing and stretching out his snout toward her. Sometimes the two animals will wrestle and seem to be biting and scratching one another as if in anger. In some other insectivores, such as the short-tailed shrew of North America, the male will utter excited clicking sounds as he importunes his mate; if she is unreceptive she will warn him off with indignant squeaks or, if pressed beyond patience, utter a high-pitched chatter.

Compared with this somewhat violent prenuptial behavior, the preliminaries to mating in such a large and formidable mammal as the elephant are remarkably gentle. According to an old Indian belief, as soon as spring comes round, the female elephant digs a pit in the ground, furnishes it with fruit and other eatables, and then lies down in it in a languorous and seductive attitude. A few soft trumpetings soon attract the attention of her mate, who descends into the pit and lies there for a month with the female in an unending embrace. Except for passing each other an occasional fruit or tender shoot, the whole period, it is alleged, is given over to the business of love-making.

This delightful concept belongs, of course, to the realms of fantasy, but the real behavior of courting elephants has a charm and delicacy that is quite exceptional in the animal world. Elephants are affectionate animals and it is not unusual for a male and female to show a marked preference for one another even before mating time comes around. When the female's season approaches, however, this friendship quickly turns to passion as the female stimulates her partner to the peak of desire. Alternately encouraging and resisting his advances, she makes provocative gestures with her body and fondles him erotically with her trunk. As the height of the love play is reached, a certain amount of grunting and subdued trumpeting may occur, but the act of copulation itself usually takes place in silence.

The mating behavior of many hoofed mammals has been well described. For instance, H. Hediger, director of the Zürich Zoo, tells how males of the beautiful impala, an African antelope which lives in large herds, make a combined approach on the females, circling them as a group and sometimes fighting among themselves as they do so. But some of the most charming courtships occur among sea mammals. Thus the male and female of the Falkland sea lion will face one another on the shore for long periods, caressing each other with sinuous movements of the neck and sometimes bringing their mouths together in a kiss. With humpback whales the love play is much more violent, and Bourlière has stated that they will swim alongside one another, giving their partners' bodies powerful whacks with their flippers and occasionally throwing themselves completely out of the water, to fall back with a loud splash.

SENTIMENTALISTS who would like to think that other mammals are capable of the prolonged monogamous relationships that sometimes characterize men and women will be disappointed to learn that this phenomenon is extremely rare. Mating in many species, and especially among such small mammals as insectivores, rodents and bats, is almost completely promiscuous and indiscriminate. After sexual union has occurred the two animals go their separate ways and may never see each other again. Parental care in such cases is provided entirely by the mother, and the father decamps to indulge his sexual desires with other equally temporary partners.

Other mammals, such as seals and deer, although not as indiscriminate in their amours as this, do not reserve their favors for one mate. Many of them are polygamous, with the males gathering harems of females during the breeding season. The Alaskan fur seal is one of these. Every spring the males arrive off the bleak Pribilof breeding grounds early in May, some weeks before the females arrive. Scrambling ashore, each adult bull establishes a beach territory which he defends against all rivals. Immature bachelor males, not yet old enough to fight for mates, bypass these activities of their elders and gather together on separate beaches. In June the females arrive, heavy with young, and each bull herds as many of them as he can into his own territory. There is constant bellowing and fighting as neighboring bulls try to steal each other's wives.

Soon after her arrival, each of the pregnant females gives birth to a pup; almost immediately thereafter she comes into heat and mates with her harem-master. He continues to guard his bevy of females with their pups throughout the summer, neither eating nor leaving his territory for several months. When fall comes, the whole herd departs from the islands and each of the sexes goes its separate way. The bulls usually head for the Gulf of Alaska, but females and young winter as far south as the coast of California. When the next spring comes, each bull will acquire a circle of mates in the same way, but his new harem may include none of his mates of the previous year.

Foxes and wolves tend to remain faithful to one mate. This fact is well known to fox breeders, who often have great difficulty in getting a male to copulate with more than one female. A high level of fidelity is also shown by certain primates, such as the lar gibbon, and by the American beaver. In these animals a monogamous relationship may be sustained for many years, if not for life.

The climax of love play is, of course, copulation itself, and this is performed in different ways by different species. Sometimes the period of union is very prolonged; ferrets, for instance, may remain together for over an hour in a single union. Alternatively, many small rodents will copulate scores of times a day, each act perhaps taking only a few seconds. The record is probably held by Shaw's jird, a small desert rodent of North Africa, which has been observed to copulate 224 times in two hours—an average of nearly twice a minute.

After it is fertilized, the mammalian egg usually begins to divide almost immediately and soon develops into a growing embryo. In the platypus and echidna, the only egg-laying mammals, a shell is deposited about the egg and it then passes out of the female's body—as happens with birds and many reptiles. The platypus lays her two or three eggs, each about a half inch in diameter, in an underground nest about two weeks after mating. Curling about the eggs, which have soft, sticky shells and adhere to one another, the female incubates them for about 10 days until the baby platypuses hatch, each of them breaking through the shell with an egg tooth which soon drops off.

The period of gestation varies greatly between one species of mammal and another. The marsupials, or pouched mammals, have the shortest gestation periods of all, ranging from as little as 8 to 12 days for the marsupial cat to 38 to 40 days for the largest kangaroos. But in these animals, of course, the young are born in a very immature condition and go through a second phase of development in the mother's pouch. The young of even such a large creature as the great gray kangaroo is only half an inch long at birth, while that of the common American opossum is the size of a honeybee and weighs two grams.

It was long thought that the mother opossum, as well as other marsupial mothers, placed the newborn young in the pouch, transporting them there with her mouth or forefeet. Careful observations, however, bear out the fact that the embryonic offspring reach the pouch under their own power, climbing with a swimming motion of forelegs and head through the fur from the vaginal orifice to the pouch opening and then scrambling in. The female, however, does usually smooth the way for them by licking a pathway through the fur. Once in the pouch, the newborn baby immediately searches for a nipple and, finding one, seizes it in its mouth and hangs on for some weeks.

In placental mammals, where the young come to a much higher degree of maturity before birth, the gestation periods are longer and are generally related to the size of the adult animal. Very small placentals may have even shorter gestation periods than large marsupials—three to four weeks for several small rodents and insectivores—but with the larger placentals the time is greatly increased. Some average gestation periods for these mammals are: a year for the zebra, 15 months for the giraffe, 18 months for the rhinoceros and 20 to 21 months for the elephant.

The gestation period, when the young mammal is developing to take its place in the world, represents a period of prenatal care on the part of the mother. This is not conscious, of course, for it is dictated by the automatic mechanisms of the body. But it does represent the first phase of a period of protective behavior by the parents, especially the mother, which continues in more obvious form after the young are born.

We are apt to regard the care which female animals give to their offspring as one of the most beautiful phenomena in nature, and certainly in such advanced

THE RATES AT WHICH YOUNG MAMMALS MATURE

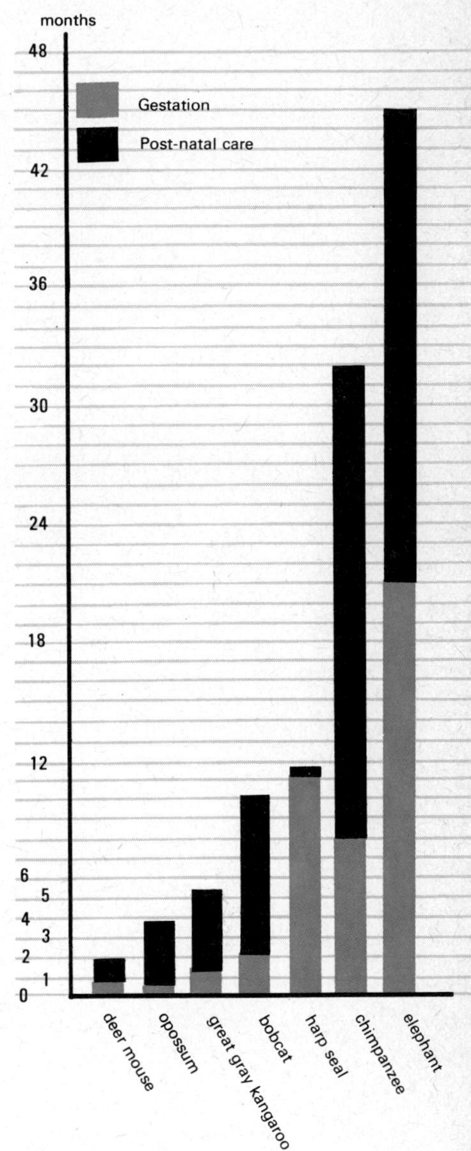

Both the time spent developing within the mother and that spent being cared for by her after birth vary enormously from species to species among the mammals. As a general rule, the smaller the animal the shorter these times will be, as shown by the deer mouse in this graph. Marsupials spend a relatively short time in the womb and considerably longer in the maternal pouch. The bobcat, like most carnivores, requires a long period of maternal care and training after birth. The harp seal, by contrast, nurses its pup on rich milk for only two weeks before abandoning it. A baby chimp must have two years of maternal care after eight months of gestation. The elephant, being the largest land mammal, has the longest gestation period.

mammals as man it does seem to contain a genuinely altruistic or spiritual element. This must not blind us to the fact, however, that the instinct to look after the offspring is very largely as mechanically determined as the nourishment of the embryo in the womb before birth. Mother love is one of the activities necessary to evolutionary survival. However touching it may sometimes seem, it owes considerably more to the built-in genetic structure of the animal than to purely altruistic motives. But whatever its origin, it takes over in full force as soon as the young are born.

Most mammals are born headfirst, though young porpoises enter the world the other way round. The female porpoise breaks the umbilical cord with a twist of her supple body and the youngster bobs to the surface for its first breath of air. From the beginning it is able to swim. Mother manatees get under their newborn young and bring them to the surface, supporting the offspring on their backs while they fill their lungs with air.

THE number of young produced by mammals at any one birth varies from one to as many as a dozen or more. Parental care occurs in every case, but is generally more developed where the number of offspring is small. Moreover, there is some correlation between brood size and the level of intelligence. Generally speaking, the more advanced an animal is in the evolutionary scale, the smaller the number of young produced at each birth. A growing sophistication in the care of the offspring replaces the more rapid and indiscriminate breeding characteristic of animals at a lower level of development. This is because the survival of the species need no longer be achieved primarily by the production of large families with a high mortality rate. Quality has replaced quantity as the main key to survival.

Most primates, being the most advanced order of mammals, usually have only one offspring at each birth, and even such comparatively lowly primates as lemurs show a remarkably advanced capacity for maternal care. Soon after the young of some lemurs are born, they cling horizontally to the lower part of the mother's abdomen, holding on to her fur with all four limbs and twisting their tails around her back for further support. The mother uses her own tail to make the infant still more secure, curling it up between her legs and around the offspring to form a natural cradle. From time to time she will sit upright and bend over her baby, making a low-pitched crooning sound which is very reminiscent of the soothing noise made by a human mother. At a later stage, lemurs, like many true monkeys, carry their young about on their backs. This method of transportation is also, incidentally, practiced by many other mammals, including creatures as different as the opossum, the giant anteater and the koala bear.

Parental care in primates continues for an exceptionally long time. The most spectacular example is man himself. The child, even in the most primitive societies, generally does not become truly independent of its parents until it is at least 12 years old. In advanced societies, where elaborate cultural traditions have to be transmitted by a protracted process of education, this period is longer still and the young human is generally not regarded as being fully emancipated until the age of 21.

In plant-eating mammals, which are the habitual quarry of predators, the exact opposite is the case. The survival of these creatures depends very largely on their ability to escape from their enemies, and therefore mobility at a very early age is essential. Rats and mice, the principal quarry of many different

MARSUPIAL MAMMALS AT BIRTH

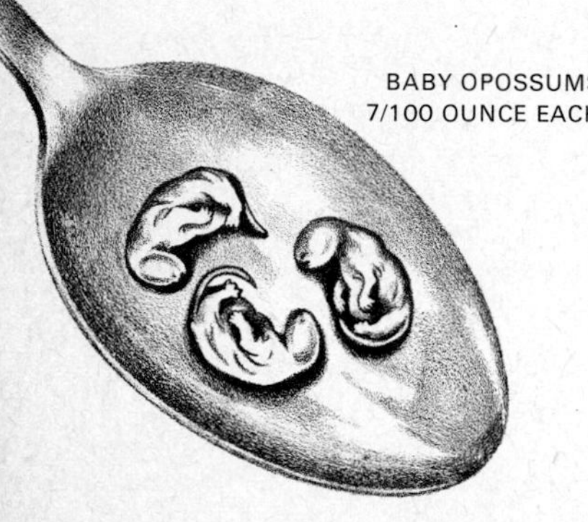

BABY OPOSSUMS 7/100 OUNCE EACH

As a general rule, marsupials spend less time in the womb than placental mammals and are born in a correspondingly less developed state. Blind and almost helpless at birth, they nevertheless do have claws and strong enough forelimbs to crawl to a nipple along a path of moistened belly hair licked flat by the mother. When a young opossum reaches a nipple, it attaches itself and does not let go for two months. Since opossums have 13 nipples, any extra babies in the litter starve and die.

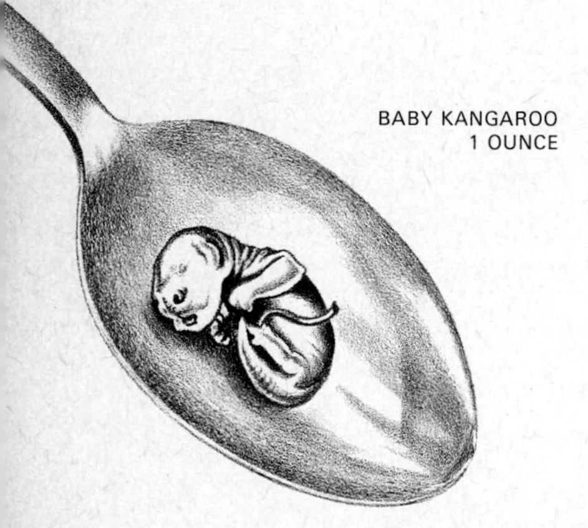

BABY KANGAROO 1 OUNCE

kinds of predators, are usually helpless at birth, but their speedy maturation helps to compensate for this initial disadvantage. Young field mice, for example, may be weaned before they are three weeks old, be independent of parents a week later and bear litters themselves by the time they are six weeks old. Survival in their perilous existence depends on growing up quickly and on having large and frequent litters. Hoofed mammals, on the other hand, usually have only one or two young each year, which are in an advanced stage of development at birth. Thus the young giraffe is able to stand within a few minutes and to run quite efficiently within two days. The same is true of young antelopes and camels, and of wild cattle, horses, sheep and goats.

By contrast, typical carnivores are born in an almost helpless condition. They are often blind for some time after birth and remain with their parents for periods ranging from several months to well over a year. A moment's thought will show the reason for this different evolutionary pattern. Young members of the cat and dog families, being predators, are not themselves in serious danger of attack, for any threat that might appear could usually be warded off by their parents. On the other hand, to become successful hunters, they must undergo a complicated process of learning and this requires a prolonged period of association between parents and offspring.

Of course, much of the behavior which leads to successful predation is instinctive, as anyone who has watched a month-old kitten stalking a piece of windblown paper will realize; but much more has to be learned by parental precept, and this is where an extended apprenticeship is so valuable.

Lions provide a good example of the way young carnivores acquire the hunting techniques essential to their survival. When they are a few months old they will accompany their parents on hunting expeditions, watching while the kill is made and then rushing in to share the spoils. After 10 months or so, however, when the canine teeth of the young lions are well developed, they begin to hunt their own prey, the parents merely standing by to give assistance if necessary. It is most intriguing to observe how, from a blundering and unconfident start, the young lion gradually grows in efficiency until it can obtain its quarry with the same skill as its parents.

ALTHOUGH sexual and family cooperation is found in an advanced state in many mammals, still more complex patterns of behavior are to be observed in mammalian societies. Social organization introduces the factor of cooperative effort as an aid to survival and is characteristic of many creatures outside the mammalian class. Many insects, for example, have highly evolved social systems, but here the specialization of different members of the group to different functions is often correlated with variations in their physical structure. Thus in a colony of harvester ants the members of the worker caste and the soldier castes differ markedly in appearance. In mammals these physical differences are hardly apparent at all, and the main benefit derived from living together in troops, packs, flocks or herds is collective defense or attack. Groups such as these are usually composed of animals with close family connections. A herd of herbivores will normally include parents and children, the parents' brothers and sisters with their children, and perhaps an occasional "in-law" which has been accepted into the group from outside. Sometimes the organization is very loose, but often the group has an acknowledged leader, which may be either a male or female, and a number of predominant adults which take precedence over younger and less experienced individuals.

PLACENTAL MAMMALS AT BIRTH

BEAR CUBS
10 OUNCES EACH

Remaining longer in the womb, the newborn young of placental mammals tend to be much larger and more fully developed than those of marsupials. Some, like bear cubs, are blind and relatively helpless. Born in the winter in a den, they nurse while their mother sleeps. When spring comes they are able to follow her into the world. The young of hoofed animals, born in the open, must be active immediately. A baby giraffe, which may be six feet tall at birth, can stand alone in a few minutes.

BABY GIRAFFE
85 POUNDS

A definite hierarchy, or "peck order," has been observed in mammals as different as baboons, Barbary sheep and bottle-nosed dolphins. At the Bronx Zoo in New York scientists have carefully worked out the hierarchy among Barbary sheep by a series of experiments. One of these was to throw a piece of bread midway between two individuals which had been previously marked for identification purposes. However often the experiment was repeated, the dominant sheep always obtained the bread, either by butting the other animal with its head or simply by making a threatening gesture. Such hierarchies become firmly established in mammalian societies, and animals lower in the social scale than the dominant individuals either move away when they approach or make submissive gestures. In wolves such gestures may take the form of cringing low on the hind legs, depressing the tail and making anxious-to-please licking movements with the tongue. If this reaction does not occur, the dominant animal will probably raise its tail and fur, bare its teeth and move threateningly toward the lower-caste individual.

A SOCIAL organization is so beneficial to its members, even when they rank low in the peck order and suffer periodical humiliation at the hands of their superiors, that they seldom voluntarily leave it. The idea of safety in numbers is a deeply ingrained instinct in the herd, and animals that disobey it usually perish, especially if they are small and, as individuals, comparatively defenseless. With larger social animals, however, it occasionally happens that one member of the herd will leave it and lead a solitary life. Solitary elephants, for instance, are by no means uncommon, and such a large animal finds no physical difficulty in surviving away from its fellows. The psychological problem must be considerable, however, and this probably at least partially accounts for the fact that such recluses are sometimes so bad-tempered and aggressive that they are commonly known as "rogues."

The reason why an elephant should leave the herd is difficult to determine. The fact that solitary elephants are usually large and therefore aged bulls suggests that they may have been driven out from the group by younger rivals who have defeated them in battle. Rheumatism and arthritis, from which elephants are known to suffer, may also partially cripple such animals so that they are unable to keep up with their fellows. Yet another possibility is that the decay of the animal's last set of molar teeth forces it to stay in the vicinity of certain soft and easily masticable foods.

Apart from solitaries, groups of two or three bull elephants are quite frequently observed at a considerable distance from the nearest herd. This has led some naturalists to believe that elephants may establish semipermanent bachelor groups, but observation has shown that the bulls nearly always rejoin their herd for such activities as drinking and bathing. The cause of their withdrawing at other times is probably to avoid being irritated by the cows and calves, rather as many of our own species retreat to all-male clubs when domestic life becomes too irksome. Although true bachelor herds do not exist, there is at least one well-established record of an all-female herd of African elephants. The members of this herd were so extremely truculent that it became known as the "suffragette herd," and they succeeded for some time in terrorizing an area of 150 square miles around Gondokoro in the southern Sudan.

Sometimes exceptionally big assemblages of elephants can be seen, totaling 200 or even more. Other mammals may also congregate in large numbers, and in the old days of the American West one writer, Colonel R. I. Dodge, tells how he rode for more than 25 miles through a continuous herd of bison, estimated to contain no less than four million individuals. In spite of appearances, however, such large groups do not represent true societies, but rather aggregations of smaller herds which have come together in search of food, water or for some other reason. In a recent piece of research conducted by Sherwood Washburn and Irven DeVore of the University of California, 450 baboons were observed around a single water hole at the same time. To an inexperienced eye these would have seemed to be one troop, but previous observations made it quite clear to the investigators that three different troops were drinking side by side. It was noticeable, incidentally, that no mixing took place even though baboons from different troops were often within a few feet of each other.

Although groups of mammals do not seem to maintain any particular order when feeding or moving about, close observation shows that they are in fact often highly organized. Washburn and DeVore discovered that as a baboon troop moves the less dominant adult males go in the van. These are followed first by females and older juveniles, then by the dominant males and nursing mothers. More females, juveniles and finally the remainder of the adult males complete the procession. This arrangement is adopted to ensure that from whichever direction a predator threatens the troop, it will first encounter the strongest members—the adult males.

If a threat does develop, the defensive organization of the troop is further strengthened by active maneuver. The females and youngsters hurry ahead, but the males continue to walk slowly so as to interpose themselves between the females and the aggressor. Whereas a single male baboon, however strong, would stand little chance against a powerful predator, a group of 20 or so is quite sufficient to keep such animals as cheetahs or even leopards at bay. This underlines the importance of the social organization of such mammals in ensuring the survival of the species.

Unlike elephants, who have often been observed to assist wounded comrades by supporting them on either side and helping them to move along, baboons are quite merciless to sick or injured members of the troop. The baboons usually move on a daily circuit of several miles between their feeding grounds and the trees where they sleep. Except for the babies, which ride on their mothers' backs, the troop never gives help to any of its members that, because of sickness or injury, are forced to lag behind.

QUITE different patterns of behavior from those which characterize baboons are found among the arboreal monkeys of the New World. The howling monkeys of tropical America live in clans of much smaller size than most troops of baboons. A typical clan consists of fewer than 20 individuals, of which three might be adult males, eight breeding females, four juveniles and three infants in arms. There is no recognized leader of the clan and the adult males share the control. As new births enlarge the clan, maturing young males will leave it from time to time. Sometimes a female accompanies a departing male, but more often he lives a solitary existence until he teams up with a partner from some other clan.

Howling monkeys are peaceful creatures, not only within the clan, but towards members of other clans. Where many other kinds of monkeys would fight, howling monkeys seem to get rid of their aggressive instincts simply by emitting the loud roaring cry which gives them their name. This they will do in chorus if another group or individual approaches, and the noise is very probably intended as a collective gesture of defense. There is, however, no evidence that their energetic shouting matches are even the prelude to physical aggression. The females of the species do not roar, but utter high-pitched yaps reminiscent of the bark of a fox terrier. They are also remarkably good mothers, nursing their offspring in their arms and carrying them during the first year of their life, hastening to pick them up if they fall from a tree and crouching over them at night to protect them from cold and rain.

Much nonsense of an anthropomorphic kind has been written about beaver colonies, but they do provide an exceptionally good example of well-organized cooperation among mammals. As nearly everyone knows, beavers habitually create artificial ponds on streams by damming them with the trunks of trees. The animals themselves live above the dam in lodges which are likewise constructed of fallen timber and mud and have underwater entrances. The trees for both dam and lodges are felled by the beavers' sharp incisor teeth and are then floated into position and cemented together with stones and earth. The dam keeps sufficient depth of water in the reservoir to prevent its freezing to the bottom in winter. The beavers can thus use the entrances to their lodges even in the coldest weather. In summer the reservoir also provides a good breeding ground for the water lilies whose pads and roots are a favorite food of the animals. In winter they feed mainly on green branches which they have previously stored on the bottom near their lodges.

THE beaver colony is very much a family setup. There is only one dominant male, which shows considerable aggressiveness toward the males in other colonies and also to young males in his own colony when they attain breeding age. In fact, the latter are eventually driven out. This usually happens when the young males are approaching two years of age, and their mother—the oldest female of the colony—is making preparations for a new litter of young. Leaving the lodge where they were born, the two-year-old males strike out on their own, searching for mates and new areas suitable for starting colonies. The yearling young remain in the old colony, but both they and their father move out of the main lodge before the new young are born. For several months they live in temporary quarters nearby, leaving the old female and her babies in sole possession of the main lodge. Most of the work of building the dams and lodges is undertaken by the male beavers, but the females also help when they are not occupied with their young.

Prairie dogs also live in family units, but these are massed together in great colonies which may extend over many acres. Each family has its own territory and outside the breeding season the sexes appear to occupy separate burrows, which they defend fiercely from attack. Nevertheless, all the prairie dogs in the colony will peaceably share the same feeding grounds, and the whistling cries given out by any individual that becomes aware of danger are of communal benefit to the whole group. The popular idea that sentinels are posted for this express purpose, however, is extremely doubtful.

The expansion of the colony is achieved in a most interesting and unusual way. When a certain number of young prairie dogs have been reared, the parents leave them in charge of the original burrow and go and dig new burrows on the outer rim of the colony. The size of the colony therefore increases by orderly stages, without overcrowding occurring in any one spot. In fact, a study of prairie-dog society might give a few useful tips to the planners now trying to organize the rapid increase of our own species.

ON THE MCNEIL RIVER A TRIO OF ALASKAN BROWN BEAR CUBS WATCHES ATTENTIVELY AS THEIR MOTHER TEACHES THEM TO CATCH SALMON

The Life of the Young

While courtship among mammals is less elaborate than among birds, no other class of creatures lavishes such care upon its young or, if necessary, spends as much time rearing them to maturity. Most mammal parents perform a great diversity of services for their offspring—grooming, feeding, transporting, protecting them and teaching them the tricks of survival in a highly competitive world.

Courtship Rites and Battles

Breeding among mammals is preceded in many species by bitter fights among males for territory, for dominance over each other and finally for possession—in some of the "harem" societies—of as many females as possible. Pronghorn harems sometimes number up to eight females, elephant seal harems up to 30. Females, on their part, can be very selective—and seductive. A tigress will parade before the tiger of her choice, running her tail across his back. Antelope does sidle up to bucks, lick their necks and sidle off again. In lower animals there is none of this activity; the role of the female is essentially passive.

SMASHING HORNS, two bighorn rams fight it out over a ewe. After squaring off 30 feet apart, the rams charge each other at full speed and meet with a crash that can be heard for hundreds of yards. They do this repeatedly until one becomes dazed or exhausted and retires from the contest.

LIP TO LIP, a male and female hippopotamus engage in a bit of wide-mouthed courtship in a Uganda river. Similar gaping is sometimes a preliminary to a fight between rival hippo bulls, who try to slash each other with their long and dangerous teeth.

BELLOWING LOUDLY, two elephant seals in an island rookery off California's coast threaten each other at the start of a battle for the custody of some females. Fighting is almost continuous during the breeding season, and combatants show many scars.

Caring For the Young

What sets mammals apart from all other animals is their long period of "childhood" and the care lavished on the young at that time by their parents. Mammalian young are not ready to face the world alone a few hours after birth, as young snakes are. They need care and protection to survive. And, as mammals, they need childhood. As one goes up the evolutionary scale, instinct plays a smaller, and intellect and training a larger, role in the life of the individual. Not only must young mammals have a period of play and development—they get it.

This varies among the mammals themselves. It is shortest among the small rodents that constitute the diet of other, larger animals. They have not the time to lavish on training. Their cycle is one of quick birth, maturity and death. Rabbits survive through agility and fecundity, traits which do not require much training.

Quite different are the carnivores—otters, raccoons, cats and dogs. In them childhood must be longer because they have so much more to learn. A young antelope needs only to be watchful, to stay near its mother and to run. But how much more complex is the training of the young lion, which, if it is to survive, must learn how to catch that antelope. Childhood for these species is a long period of association with parents, during which they learn by observing and by being coaxed and persuaded.

NURSING A LITTER, a deer mouse lies on her side to accommodate her youngsters. Common throughout the United States, deer mice take about three weeks to bear young. In six weeks the offspring are weaned and a month later are sexually mature. Mice live only about a year, but during that time they can produce scores of offspring to replace those taken by predators.

GROOMING ONE BABY, a raccoon mother props herself up at the foot of a tree, while the rest of her brood feed on. Raccoons will dispense such care for as long as a year, not only to their own young, but to orphaned raccoons as well. Since males tend to wander, the tough and resourceful females must be the protectors of their families against marauders like dogs and owls.

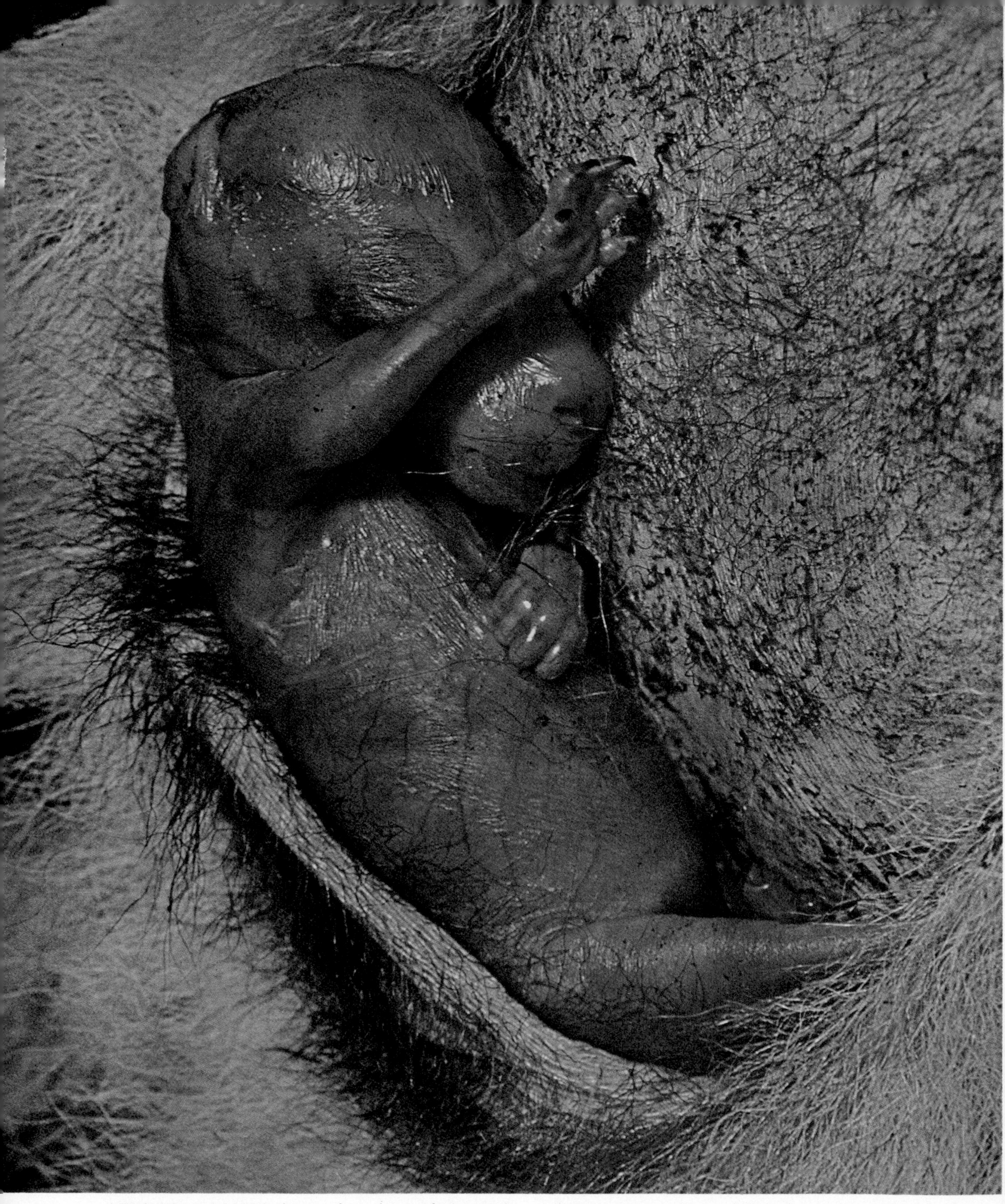

A TWO-INCH KANGAROO, almost unformed except for its mouth and forefeet, attaches itself to a nipple in its mother's pouch. In contrast to placental mammals of equivalent size, the kangaroo, like other marsupials, spends little time in the womb. Born in only five or six weeks, kangaroos grope through their mother's fur to her pouch, where they stay until development is complete.

AT FIVE MONTHS, a young kangaroo weighs about 10 pounds, but will still fit in its mother's fur-lined pocket. It is now old enough to begin tentatively exploring the world outside, but will scurry back when danger threatens, as the mother opens the pouch by bending forward. When hard pressed by wild dogs, mothers will sometimes unload their babies to save themselves.

SWINGING FREE, a baby raccoon, like many other carnivores, is unhurt when carried this way, for the skin of its nape is loose.

WALKING UPRIGHT, a beaver cradles its baby in its arms. This erect posture is easy for beavers, which sit up to gnaw trees.

GRIPPING TIGHTLY with its fingers, toes and tail, a rhesus monkey curls under its mother's belly as she heads for a nearby tree.

Transporting the Brood

An important factor in the survival of mammals is their ability to move their young in case of danger. The methods used are astonishingly varied: babies are carried on nearly every part of the body—on tails, on bellies, in mouths and cradled in the arms. In addition young bats cling to their mothers' nipples or fur with their teeth, while the three-toed sloth supports its offspring on its body as it hangs, hammock-fashion, from a branch.

Carrying is not possible for large grazing animals, which are sizable at birth, and they must rely on their offspring's instinct to move when they move and stop when they stop. For them, running is all-important to escape predators. The young of antelope and wildebeest are extremely agile at two days, and a two-week-old caribou can outrun its mother.

A COMMON SHREW LEADS HER BROOD IN SINGLE FILE ACROSS A FIELD AS EACH OF THE YOUNGSTERS MOUTHS A TUFT OF FUR ON THE REAR OF THE

RIDING SECURELY, a young pangolin digs its claws into the scales at the base of its mother's tail. When the pair is threatened, the mother stops abruptly, curls up around her baby and presents an almost invulnerable ball of scales to her enemies.

HANGING ON with feet and tail, a brood of opossum babies, too large to fit in the mother's pouch, is transported through a thicket. Young opossums normally spend two months in the pouch, then stay in close association with their mother for 40 days more.

ONE IN FRONT OF IT. THE FAMILY MAY BE SEARCHING FOR EARTHWORMS, EASY PREY FOR THESE TINY MEAT EATERS IN THEIR FIRST WEEKS OF LIFE

Keeping the Family Safe

Maternal care is highly developed among mammals. As the young grow older and begin to explore their environment, the parent must be prepared not only to teach but often to get its offspring out of trouble. Howler monkeys set up an infernal din when a baby falls out of a tree, possibly to scare away predators. Later the mother may risk descending to the ground to retrieve her baby. Cats, both wild and domestic, can be seen literally showing their young how to get out of the trees they are stuck in, continually

GETTING DOWN ON HER KNEES AND BRACING HERSELF ON THE BANK, A MOTHER ELEPHANT EXTENDS HER TRUNK TOWARD HER BABY, WHO HAS AN

climbing up and down in front of a stranded kitten, all the while mewing to comfort and encourage it. Porpoises support small, weak babies at the surface of the water so that they can breathe.

Among some species, the weak or maimed are abandoned or ruthlessly destroyed. But in others an injured infant may get special care, as in the case of the crippled baby elephant shown here, who was helped across a river and up a slippery bank by its mother while another female stood guard above.

INJURED LEG AND CANNOT CLIMB WITHOUT HELP

A STRONG TUG and the baby struggles up the bank *(above)*, to be caressed and groomed by its mother *(below)*. The elephant herd crosses and recrosses this river repeatedly for food, and the mother has a 45-minute struggle with its baby each time.

WITH SOME DIFFICULTY a young porcupine solves the complicated problem of swinging itself up over a branch. In another few weeks, with constant practice, such a feat will be almost automatic. While they forage widely on the ground, porcupines spend much time in trees, whose soft inner bark is a favorite food. They also sleep in trees, curled up in a comfortable crotch.

The Game of Growing Up

The skills that allow an adult mammal to survive the pressures of its environment are not wholly instinctive, and the young must learn many of them while still under the protection of the parents. For most immature mammals, becoming a serious adult is, ironically, a game in which they play at the real thing. Thus bear cubs join in mock battles and wrestling matches which prepare them for adult conflicts; young cats of all kinds pounce on almost anything that moves; colts and calves engage in running games; and young goats jump up and down on rocks, gaining in sure-footedness as they play.

TWO YOUNG MINKS trail behind their mother as she hunts for crayfish in a brook near her den. For minks, as for most mammals, the example of the parent is enormously important in training. The same thing done over and over will impress itself on the young. These minks are getting a lesson in thoroughness, for adults must learn to leave no stone unturned in hunting.

TEN BABY OPOSSUMS TEST THEIR CLIMBING ABILITY IN A TREE, AS ONE TRIES OUT ITS PREHENSILE TAIL

AN AFRICAN POTTO, low on the scale of living primates, clings to a tree with powerful paws. A toe on each foot is tipped by a long grooming claw, instead of the flat nails that protect most primates' digits.

8

Toward Man

MAN, as everyone now recognizes, is a mammal. Yet as recently as 100 years ago it would have been unusual to include man in a book on mammals, and to thus admit his kinship with the so-called "brute creation," without laying oneself open to a charge of blasphemy. At that time it was still widely believed that the earth was the product of a six-day creation and that all the plants and animals inhabiting it had been created by God solely for the material benefit and spiritual delectation of the human species. Since that time, of course, man has discovered, through science, a view of the actual details of the development of life on earth, and most thoughtful minds now recognize that man has evolved by the same majestic processes that have characterized the development of his plant and animal cousins.

The likenesses between man and other mammals are most obvious when we compare him with other advanced members of the primate order. Here, in fact, there are such close similarities, even in superficial aspects of physique, that it must be quite clear to reflective people that they cannot be coincidental. It is not at all surprising that the monkey house at any zoo is one of the most popular attractions: the human visitors recognize at once that monkeys and apes

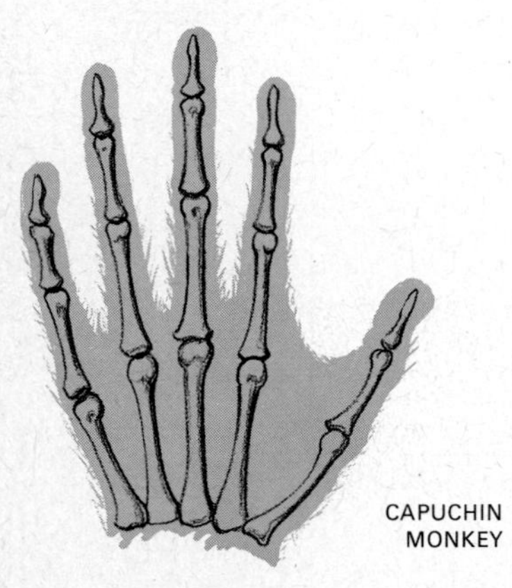

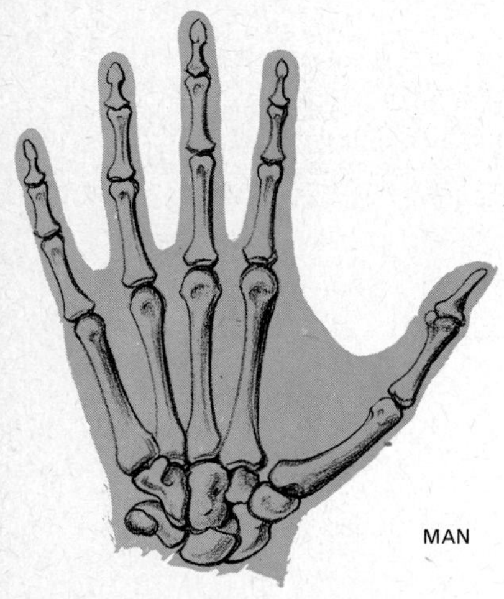

THE OPPOSABLE THUMB

Among the lowest of primates—the tree shrews—the thumb is not opposable. Unable to rotate in its socket and with a claw at its tip, its use as a grasping instrument is extremely limited. Among monkeys, the thumb is larger, set at an angle from the hand, and can be rotated in such a way as to be used with the other fingers to pick up objects. In man this adaptation has progressed remarkably. The thumb is much larger and stronger and set at a wider angle for maximum freedom of movement.

are animals that look and behave very much like themselves and that many amusing parallels can be drawn. The anthropoid apes, represented by the gorilla, chimpanzee, orangutan and the gibbons, show particularly obvious resemblances in these respects. The very name orangutan is Malayan for "man of the woods." The similarities between other primates and man have also been the subject of comment on many occasions. Thus the famous British traveler Sir Richard Burton records in 1864 that Negroes who saw him for the first time in East Africa called out: "Look at the white man; does he not look like a white ape!" To take another example, the langur is referred to in the Vedas, the sacred scriptures of Hinduism, as *Pathagahapueka*, or "the one without a loin cloth," showing that it was assumed to have close human affinities.

THE science of comparative anatomy confirms the feelings we all have that man, apes and monkeys are closely related. The human skeleton contains exactly the same number of bones as that of a gorilla or chimpanzee and even in lower primates, where the actual numbers differ, the general arrangement is very much the same. Additional evidence comes from the structures of the limbs, especially the forelimbs, which in all but the lowest primates are exceptionally well adapted for grasping; from the mobile face, so reminiscent of our own; and indeed from the correspondence of almost every organ possessed by subhuman primates to those found in man. Most significant of all, perhaps, is the evidence based on brain structure. The brains of man, monkeys and apes are identical in basic plan, and the superiority of the human intellect is dependent not upon the possession of new parts which other primates lack but only upon differences in proportions between the various parts and upon functional refinements. Thus an anatomist, with very good reason, could justly claim that our "humanity" very largely depends on the possession of an exceptionally efficient cerebral cortex, the region of the brain which confers an advanced capacity for the organization of experience.

Moreover, although man's mammalian affinities are most obviously revealed in relation to other primates, they can also be discerned by comparing him with mammals at a much lower level of evolutionary development. As we have already seen, such physiological characteristics as warm-bloodedness and the nourishment of the young by milk glands are possessed by man and all other mammals and are clear evidence of kinship. But this kinship can also be demonstrated in more dramatic form by comparing skeletal structure. Thus the limb bones of mammals as different in appearance and way of life as the horse, the sea lion and the bat are all strictly comparable. The same method can also be used to demonstrate the kinship of man with all other vertebrates. By the simple fact of possessing a vertebral column, or backbone, man clearly reveals his relationship not only with all other mammals, but with the birds, reptiles, amphibians and fishes as well.

The study of man's early evolutionary history is one of the main ways to understanding the special character he has as a mammal. This has been pieced together during the last hundred years by applying the principles governing all evolutionary change to the study of human and prehuman fossils. Many details of the story are, of course, still controversial because there are a number of important gaps in the record. Different students also vary in the significance they attach to different pieces of evidence. In general, however, the sequence of events is clear and fully accepted by those qualified to judge the evidence. The whole human experiment and all man's vast achievements have only been made possible because of a chain of biological events which started in the Age of Reptiles, when the first mammals, small creatures of the undergrowth, were scurrying to keep out of the way of their giant reptilian contemporaries. All were experimenting with different techniques of survival, and a particularly effective one adopted by the ancestors of man was to take to the trees. When the Age of Mammals dawned, a whole group of small ancestral primates, including early tree shrews, tarsiers and lemurs, were well established in the treetops.

Now to live successfully in such an unstable environment, a number of special physical adaptations were necessary. First, the extremities of the limbs, the feet and digits, had to become specialized for grasping boughs instead of for walking on the flat surface of the earth. Second, a differentiation in function between the fore and hind limbs was of great advantage—the forelimbs would clearly be most efficient if they were exceptionally flexible so as to be able to reach forward and upward to obtain new holds, while the hind limbs would achieve greater usefulness with a thicker and more muscular structure to support the weight of the body in the climbing position. Third, the need to judge distances in jumping from branch to branch gave a great advantage to animals possessing what is known as "binocular vision"—that is to say, eyes that were placed in a single forward-looking plane, enabling each to focus together on the same object, rather than being located on either side of the head with each eye covering an independent field. Lastly, and most important, the need to move efficiently through the swaying branches favored a modification of the brain, particularly an enlargement of the regions which coordinate the data transmitted by the senses of sight and touch.

If we look at living primates, and also at the fossilized bones of their ancestors, we shall see that all or most of these specializations were generally acquired to a quite spectacular extent. Now what is the significance of this in the story of man?

Sometime in the Miocene epoch, it seems, a number of primates that had gone through a successful tree-dwelling phase were returning to the ground. The climatic evidence suggests that this was caused by a reduction in the number of forests, leading to increased competition for the available living space. Among these emigrants were almost certainly our own ancestors, and the physical specializations that they had acquired during their arboreal phase were to be of immense significance to them in their new circumstances on the ground. By selective processes operating on a particular primate line that was to lead to man, the muscular hind limbs of the tree dweller became transformed into the strong supporting legs which enable man to adopt a two-legged gait. This in turn helped free the forelimbs, already well suited for grasping, for the manipulation of objects and the making of weapons and other tools. Still more important, the modifications of the brain which had occurred when our ancestors began to coordinate their senses for arboreal locomotion were equally well suited to the development of intelligence and quick-wittedness in the new world they were now invading.

The development of the primate brain in the ancestors of man, which permitted the diversion of evolutionary energy from primarily physical into primarily mental channels, was one of the greatest break-throughs in the history of life. It did not represent just another adaptation within the old physical formulas, although of course it originated through the normal laws of natural selection, but the beginning of a new *kind* of evolution operating at a new level.

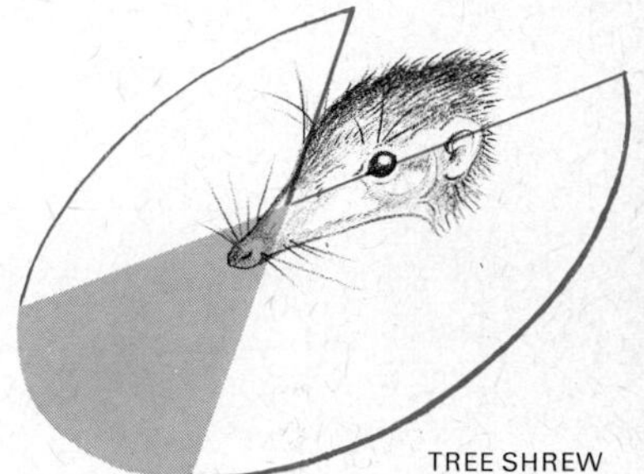

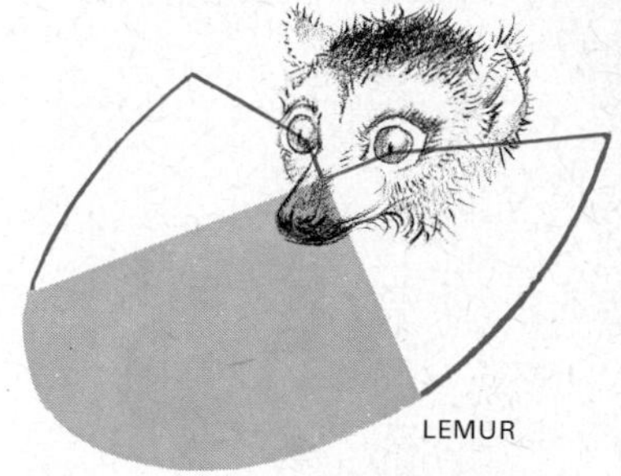

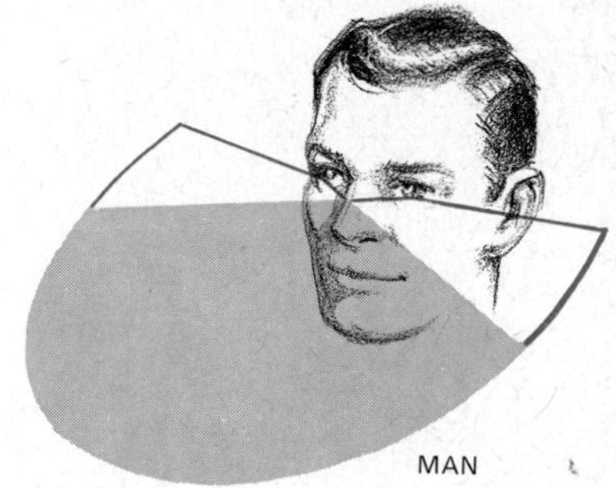

BINOCULAR VISION

Depth perception in animals is most acute where the fields of view of both eyes overlap to give what is known as binocular vision. Tree shrews, squirrel-like in appearance and habits, have a rather small area of overlap but can see well to the sides and rear. Among the more advanced primates, with larger brains and opposable thumbs, there is more handling of objects and a correspondingly greater need for good depth perception. This is supplied by the forward placement of the eyes.

Instead of being the victim of blind forces, man was now able to grow gradually in awareness until the point was reached where he actually began to understand the laws of evolution itself.

This new evolutionary level may be aptly termed psychosocial evolution—the stage where the development of self-conscious awareness gives an entirely new measure of control over the environment. Man is the only animal to have made the transition to this new phase, where he can now, if he wishes, largely determine the lines which his physical, mental and social development should follow. It lies within his powers, if he uses them wisely, not simply to record his history as if it consisted of predetermined events, but to shape it with a good understanding of the laws which govern change.

The evolutionary break-through which saw the dawn of psychosocial evolution is vastly more important than even such earlier break-throughs as were made when the amphibians evolved from the fishes, the reptiles from the amphibians and so on. Moreover, it is a development which was only made possible by the adaptations, particularly in the brain, acquired by man's arboreal ancestors of 50 million years ago, and the uses to which they put them when they came down to the ground.

AN EARLY PRIMATE

Notharctus, known from 58-million-year-old fossils found in Wyoming, represents an early stage in primate evolution somewhere between the tree shrews and the monkeys. It was one of the first primates to have a "thumb" set clearly apart from its other toes. Small, furry and active, Notharctus was a tree-dwelling animal that probably fed on fruits, seeds and insects. It is an ancestor of the modern lemur.

THE actual stages by which man's ancestors evolved throughout the Age of Mammals cannot be followed with great exactness, owing to the fact that primate fossils are always much less common than those of other mammals. This is partly because, even when they have become mainly ground dwellers, primates normally live in or near forested areas, and conditions in these regions do not encourage the preservation of bone in fossil form. Another reason is that primates are very active and intelligent creatures which seldom suffer death by drowning, and this, as we have seen, is one of the main ways in which the remains of animals come to be preserved in rock sediments. Nevertheless, several intriguing fossils have survived which belong to advanced anthropoid apes very close to the human line of descent. These include two creatures known respectively as *Dryopithecus* (the tree ape), whose remains have been found mainly in the Siwalik Hills of India, and *Proconsul* (a name derived from "Consul," a famous chimpanzee that once lived at the London Zoo), found in the Victoria Nyanza region of East Africa. Both of these fossils date from Miocene times, and even if they are not in the direct ancestral line leading to man they certainly have an excellent claim to be regarded as our very intimate relations. Later came other creatures of a much more manlike type, especially *Australopithecus*, the "southern ape" of Africa; *Pithecanthropus*, the "man-ape" of Asia; and still later, Neanderthal man, a true man of Europe and the Middle East.

In the context of geological time, the stages by which our species has evolved to its present state have been extremely swift. This speed of development has, of course, been largely instrumental in giving man his present advantage over his mammalian competitors. At the same time, however, it has been responsible for certain failures in physical adjustment, for if we consider our bodies today we shall find that they show several grave imperfections. For example, the adoption of an upright stance has thrown a severe strain on the body wall, which is now called upon to support the internal organs in unusual positions. This is why our species is inclined to develop hernias, or ruptures, from which our primate ancestors probably seldom suffered. Again the upright stance, combined with the rapid lengthening of the hind legs, has caused varicose veins to become increasingly common due to the weight of blood in long, vertically extended columns. The frequent need for Caesarean operations is also evidence that the size of the mother's birth canal has not kept pace with the rapid enlargement of the human cranium to accommodate man's expanding brain.

In spite of his imperfections, man has nevertheless succeeded in triumphing over other mammals which would seem to have better physical equipment. In feeding habits he is particularly versatile and this has been a great aid to his survival. His teeth are not specialized for dealing with any one type of food as is the case with strictly carnivorous or herbivorous mammals, the canines in particular being very much reduced. Thus meats, made tender by cooking, raw or cooked vegetables, nuts and fruits and many other substances are equally suitable to him as a source of nourishment.

At this point an important question arises. Teeth, we know, are an exceptionally valuable part of the offensive equipment of many mammals, and the canines of a carnivore are particularly useful in the killing of its prey. While it is easy to understand that human teeth are quite adequate for dealing with vegetable nourishment, we may well ask how man overcame the handicap of reduced canines in obtaining animal food. The answer is twofold. First, the immense development of the human brain, leading to increased intelligence, enabled man to substitute tools and weapons for structures that in lower mammals form part of the body itself. Man may lack canines as hunting weapons, but his reasoning powers enabled even his primitive ancestors to make spears, darts, clubs and other weapons which were even more effective in killing his quarry. Secondly, this same sophisticated brain enabled man to domesticate certain animals so that they were always available for his use. Increased intelligence released him from the precariousness of the old hunting economy practiced by his ancestors, and his survival became assured by a thoughtful exploitation of both animals and plants under controlled conditions rather than the random and often chancy results of the chase.

Similar intriguing ideas are related to the locomotion of man compared with that of the lower mammals. Man is the only strictly bipedal mammal that has ever lived on the earth. His upright stance was made possible by evolutionary modifications in the hind limbs, which caused the sole to become larger and more flattened as compared with that of other primates. The limbs themselves also grew proportionately longer. In the earlier stages of human evolution the elongation of the hind limbs and the ability to stand upright conferred several straightforward biological advantages. Increased height, for instance, allowed for a longer range of vision, for spotting either enemies or prey, and here again the brain was of paramount importance in enhancing this advantage.

MAN has not surpassed his fellow mammals in the field of locomotion because he exceeds them in height or in running ability; he is, in fact, greatly inferior to many other mammals in these respects. But just as increased intelligence enabled him to make weapons for obtaining food, so it led him to invent extracorporeal equipment which increased his capacity for movement. Man is the only mammal able to build machines that will transport him through every medium far more quickly and efficiently than even the most specialized locomotor equipment possessed by less-advanced members of the class. This ability depends entirely on the power of his brain and is not related to any purely locomotor modification of his body as such.

Attack and defense in mammals have already been discussed, and only a few paragraphs back we saw how the hunting weapons invented by primitive man

MAN'S VERSATILITY AS AN INVENTOR OF IMPLEMENTS

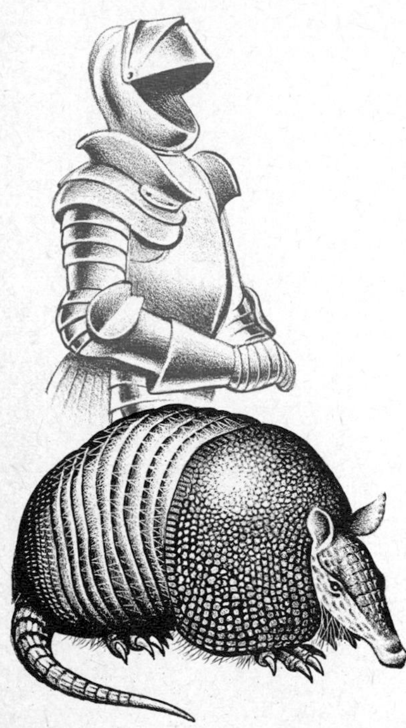

By specializing in intelligence, man has escaped the need to evolve the variety of special bodily structures that other animals depend on for survival. For defense, the armadillo (above) has a permanent suit of bony armor. To eat, the wart hog (below) digs with its enlarged tusks. But man, in such situations, has devised armor that can be put on and taken off and a pickax that can be picked up and laid aside. He does this with the same hand and arm—free to use any other tool that his brain invents.

became a substitute for the specialized teeth which less-advanced mammals so largely use to obtain their prey. But it is now possible to go further and show how man invented other extracorporeal equipment as a substitute for many other kinds of aggressive and defensive structures possessed by mammals. Knives and daggers, for instance, serve the same aggressive purpose as the giant canines possessed by stabbing cats. Even more obvious examples crop up when we consider some of the devices man has used to defend himself from aggressors. Thus the armor used by soldiers in classical and medieval times duplicates very exactly the protective coverings possessed by armadillos and pangolins. In fact, the very way in which the metal of man-made armor is jointed to conform with the configuration of the human body in many cases almost exactly duplicates the arrangement found in the armadillo's protective covering. A more up-to-date example is to be found in the modern armor-plated tank, which also demonstrates man's capacity for evolving new types of locomotor equipment. Suits of mail and armor-plated tanks simply represent projections of a defensive technique—which armadillos had already adopted at the biological level—into the consciously controlled *mental* level of evolution which is distinctive of man.

SIMILAR examples of this process can be found when we consider how camouflage has been used by man as an aid to defense. Thus the green or mottled battledress worn by modern jungle-fighting soldiers is specifically designed to render the soldier inconspicuous against the background of lush tropical vegetation. The color patterns used to conceal aircraft hangars and other military buildings from the attack of enemy bombers are another obvious example of man's use of camouflage. The importance of expert knowledge of the biological basis of camouflage in such circumstances is shown, incidentally, by the fact that a number of the world's leading authorities on animal coloration have advised the belligerents in all the major wars of this century.

In addition to camouflage, men have also utilized the ways by which several mammals make use of warning coloration and other aids to clear identification. Conspicuousness, rather than concealment, may sometimes be valuable as a survival technique. Man has made use of this fact, as is particularly well demonstrated in the uniforms worn by law-enforcement officers. Thus the tall helmet of the British policeman or the distinctive hat and dress of his colleague in the United States are visual symbols which say, in effect: "I am an individual with special powers. It would be dangerous to argue with me and even more dangerous to attack me." This is an oversimplification, of course, for other factors, such as simple recognition, also play a part. Nevertheless, society has recognized that such symbols tend to inspire awe and discourage assault. Because of this, they are effective aids to social stability and therefore assist in the survival of the species as a whole.

Further intriguing comparisons can be made between man and his fellow mammals in the fields of sexual behavior and social organization. With most mammalian species, where sexual and social attitudes are almost entirely the result of biological determinants, there is a great uniformity of behavior over the whole range of each individual species. Thus individuals of such cosmopolitan and wide-ranging mammals as the house mouse and common rat all adopt very similar patterns of sexual and social behavior, whether they live in the Old or New Worlds, in the tropics or in far northern regions. With man, however, there is a very wide range of differences, and such contrasted systems as monogamy and polygamy, patriarchy and matriarchy, and (in the field of economics) capitalism and communism may be found operating perfectly satisfactorily in different environments. The reason for this is basically the same as that which determines the differences between patterns of behavior in food getting, locomotion, attack and defense and other matters. *Cultural* processes have become more important than built-in biological patterns and a far greater range of adaptation is thereby achieved. Nevertheless, the attitudes of man the mammal to sex and society still often reveal their biological roots.

The primary basis of attraction between men and women is not related to the oestrous period, which is the main stimulus to mating among so many other mammals. Our species, like higher primates in general, is prepared to mate at any time of the year, even though some romantics still believe that it is mainly in the spring that "a young man's fancy lightly turns to thoughts of love." Nevertheless, many of the techniques used by the two sexes to attract each other are remarkably like those used by other kinds of mammals. Sensory stimuli are, in fact, quite as important in mating behavior among members of our own species as they are in some of the mammals described in this book.

The erotic kiss practiced by humans is a particularly good example of the way in which the senses of touch, smell and taste may be combined in a single stimulus to sexual union. Visual signals are also very effective in man as in other mammals, as is shown by the wearing of beards as symbols of virility by young men and of décolleté dresses by girls to reveal as much of the breasts as the law allows. Several other refinements devised by man's evolving brain are less obviously but just as surely intended to encourage sexual rapprochement. Thus jewelry and make-up, which have always been used by women as aids to allure, are simply a sophisticated substitute for the visual stimuli built into the bodies of many other kinds of mammals. Perfume is another example, being an artificial extension of the olfactory signals for which mammals at a lower level of evolution must rely on the secretions of certain scent glands. In the field of movement, the provocative dances practiced by primitive peoples, and also quite often by members of more sophisticated societies, certainly have a sexual basis, even though they are sometimes disciplined and sublimated—as in a ballet—to a point where the connection is not always recognized.

IN the organization of society itself man shows an enormous advance over any other species of mammal. In fact it is the recognition of the value of cooperative effort that has been mainly responsible for bringing him to his present dominant position. Various mammals cooperate with one another as we have seen. They may practice collective hunting, as in wolves and hunting dogs; family hunting, as in lions; or may simply live in defensive aggregations of various sizes, as baboons and many species of herbivores do. In such cases, however, except for the peck order, which encourages the survival of the more dominant individuals, there is very little specialization of roles. Even the idea that certain animals such as elephants or prairie dogs post sentinels or send out scouts is extremely suspect. If it occurs at all, it is certainly not characteristic of mammals in general.

With man, however, the specialization of individuals for different functions has reached a very high degree of perfection. To take an immediate example, as the author of this book I was responsible for assembling the text and presenting it in as readable a form as possible. However, that was by no means the whole story. Another man edited it and certainly improved it in many ways; many others illustrated it; others again printed it and bound it; finally, its presentation to the reader was made possible only by the competence of a whole series of other experts, specialized in the techniques of advertising, publicity, bookselling, display and distribution.

This cooperative effort based on highly developed role specialization runs through the whole of human society and is one diagnostic character of man as a mammal. That is why, when it breaks down, either on a small scale as in localized industrial disputes or on a large scale as in war, the species in general experiences emotions that range from apprehension to terror. The immense complexities of our social organization, consciously organized through the intelligence of our advanced primate brains, are essential to the survival of the species. A failure to maintain this organization could lead to total extinction.

A number of important ways in which man either resembles or differs from his mammalian cousins have now been considered. How can we best sum the whole matter up and define the significance of man's role among the mammals? The class as a whole, we have seen, represents a higher stage of evolutionary progress than that attained by any other. Control within wide limits of the body temperature, care of the young extending over long periods, the transmission of acquired learning, increased intelligence and, in some species, a strong tendency to socialization are specially characteristic of the group and have conferred important advantages upon it. Man, in these respects, is strictly comparable with other mammals. His body is built on the same plan, he reproduces by the same means and his biological development both before and after birth closely resembles that of the higher primates. Moreover, many aspects of human behavior can trace back their origins to the instinctive behavior of mammals at a much lower level of evolution.

WHAT, then, distinguishes the human species from other mammals? To answer in a single phrase, it is the power of conceptual thought. We have seen how the development of the cortical region of the brain, combined with the freeing of the forelimbs for other activities by the adoption of an upright stance, led to the manufacture of tools. But what we may not have realized is that toolmaking requires a new *kind* of thought altogether. A chimpanzee may use a stick to reach a banana lying beyond its grasp, and the stick in this case becomes a tool of a kind. But for early man to sit down and flake a stone into an arrowhead for use in the hunt required the capacity to envisage an *imaginary future situation* where it would prove useful. This ability to think in abstract concepts rather than simply to react to immediate concrete stimuli is the key to the difference between man and other mammals. It is the essential requirement which must precede not only toolmaking, but fire making, speech, writing, conscious role specialization in society and all the other fundamental activities which distinguish man from his fellow mammals. And at a higher level, it is a prerequisite of the development of the whole of his technological, scientific, artistic and philosophical thought.

To amplify these points would take us far beyond the scope of a general introduction to mammals, but they do show how essential it is to relate our species to the rest of nature if we are to understand our present role in life. In particular, by studying the evolutionary history of mammals and comparing ourselves with living members of the group, it is possible to see that natural history and human history are not separate departments of knowledge, but parts of a single process. To study mammals is, to a very large extent, to study our own past.

THOUGH THEY BEAR A CLOSE RESEMBLANCE TO SQUIRRELS, THE LIVELY TREE SHREWS ARE ACTUALLY THE MOST PRIMITIVE LIVING PRIMATES

The Primates

From an unlikely start as active little creatures that lived in trees, the primates have radiated into a variety of successful types. They are a curious evolutionary mixture; the development of sharp vision and grasping hands and a tremendous growth of the brain have given them a unique combination of specialized talents while permitting them to remain remarkably unspecialized in other ways.

NIGHT VISION of the potto is intensified by a special layer of cells behind the retina at the back of the eyeball. This layer contains guanine crystals; light passing through the retinal cells is reflected back again by the guanine, doubling its effectiveness. Although it sees well at night, the potto moves so slowly it has earned the native nickname "softly-softly."

THE HUGE EYES of the South American night monkey, or douroucoulis, have pupils that can expand enormously in the dark. Its head shows several important primate characteristics: a flatter muzzle, indicating less dependence on smell and more on sight; forward-facing eyes for good depth perception; and a more rounded skull for greater brain capacity.

OPPOSABLE THUMBS on both hand and foot are displayed by a drill. Although the drill can pick up objects quite easily with its feet, it is a ground-dwelling animal, more adapted to walking flat-footed than to holding onto branches the way the orangutan does. A more specialized foot is exhibited by man, whose big toes are not opposable and are now useless for gripping.

Versatile Limbs and Grasping Paws

Primates today have limbs that set them apart from other mammals. One difference is that the joint between the arm and shoulder allows their arms to move freely in all directions. An even more important structure is the primate's opposable thumb, with which it can grasp a branch firmly. Taken together, these enable tree dwellers to move about with considerable ease and speed—some of the smaller primates on all fours and the larger gibbons and orangutans often by swinging from branch to branch by their arms. The hands that at first grasped tree branches were equally well adapted to picking and holding food, and later on to manipulating objects. This dexterity foreshadowed the use of tools and weapons, which were indeed developed by one kind of primate—long after he descended from the trees.

MUNCHING LEAVES, A BABY ORANGUTAN GRIPS WITH HANDS AND FEET AS IT DESCENDS A TREE

Emotions and Their Expression

Do other animals feel the emotions that humans do? We can only speculate about this, although one basic assumption seems reasonable: complexity of emotional life is fairly obviously connected with mental capacity. Among the lowest animals, such as worms and jellyfish, whose brains are either absent or very simple, emotions are probably entirely lacking. Lizards and fish may experience dim feelings of anger or alarm. It is only when one gets up among the mammals that a wide spectrum of emotions becomes a possibility, and only at this point that emotion begins to be expressed in an animal's face. Here, too, intelligence is a critical factor; a porcupine is not only far stupider but also far less expressive than a chimpanzee. The latter, while it may reveal a variety of feelings, may not be doing so in a way that is recognizable to humans. To know what a chimp is feeling, one should know the chimp.

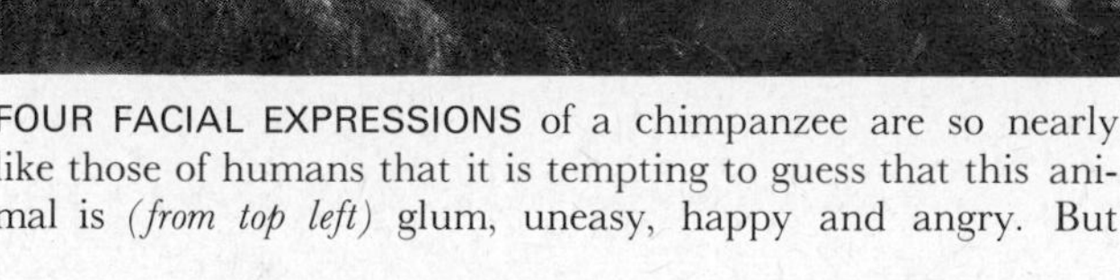

FOUR FACIAL EXPRESSIONS of a chimpanzee are so nearly like those of humans that it is tempting to guess that this animal is *(from top left)* glum, uneasy, happy and angry. But chimps do not necessarily express their feelings as men do, and dangerous misinterpretations can be made. For example, a level stare, innocuous in humans, may express hostility in some apes.

A GORILLA HAS A MORE LIMITED FACIAL REPERTOIRE THAN A CHIMPANZEE, BUT IT CAN SHED TEARS

IN TESTS OF IMITATIVE ABILITY, VIKI, A FOUR-YEAR-OLD CHIMPANZEE, CAN UNDERSTAND "DO THIS" SPOKEN BY HER "MAMA" AND SUCCESSIVELY

What a Chimpanzee Can and Cannot Learn

Neither flexibility, versatile limbs nor stereoscopic vision alone could have brought about the transformation of the primates without still another factor, the extraordinary growth of the forebrain which underlies intelligence. The living primates closest to man are the great apes. And of these, the chimpanzees, because of their affectionate and sociable natures and close physiological resemblance to man, have been the most studied. Viki, adopted "daughter" of psychologists Keith and Cathy Hayes, was brought up from birth with the same care as a human infant. At first she learned faster than human children, but by the age of four they were about equal. Then no amount of further training could make up for her lack of language. At the age when adult speech opens new worlds to the human child,

VIKI LIGHTS A CIGARETTE for Dr. Hayes, taking care not to burn her fingers. At four years she had learned many household tasks and could wring out the wash, scrub tiles, push a dust mop, and use tools such as a saw and a screwdriver. She had also learned four words: "mama," "papa," "cup" and "up." Viki was one of the few chimpanzees ever to master any words.

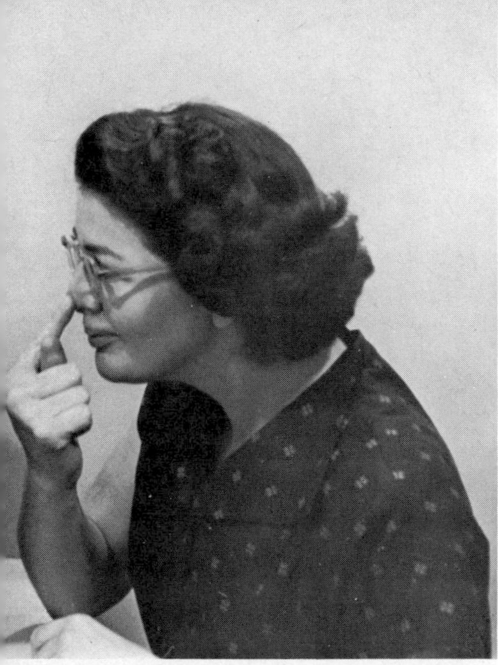

LIFTS HER EYEBROWS, TOUCHES HER NOSE AND CLAPS HANDS. BY IMITATION SHE COULD LEARN MANY SKILLS SHE COULD NOT BE TAUGHT IN WORDS

Viki had about reached the limits of her learning.

Bright baboons were taught to pick fruit and stack wood in ancient Egypt. In Sumatra macaques collect coconuts for their owners. Recently in Australia a rhesus monkey learned how to herd sheep and steer a tractor for its owner. But neither ape nor talented monkey can pass on such "cultural" skills to their offspring without the power of speech.

VIKI HAS SUPPER, eating her bananas and grapes neatly with a spoon. Sweets were used to encourage her to solve problems in scientific experiments and also as rewards for a job well done.

VIKI LISTENS IN on a party-line telephone. Although she enjoyed adding a few grunts and squeals to liven up the human conversations, she did not herself say words or answer "hello's."

A HUNGRY CHIMP shows intelligence by solving a problem it has not previously faced. Unable to get the bananas hanging beyond its reach in the picture at left, it puts a crate under them *(center)* to stand on. When this does not work, it piles up three boxes to make a stand of sufficient height—and gets its reward.

Reason, Insight and Problem Solving

As yet there is no simple definition of intelligence. In man it has been described as an ability to think abstractly, although some scientists prefer to define it as the organism's ability to adjust successfully to its environment. Much of the behavior called intelligent in lower animals is actually the result of reflex or instinctive actions. Yet some animals, especially the higher apes, do at times display intelligent behavior as we know it in man, clearly showing some understanding of cause and effect, and also the ability to solve problems which are entirely new in their experience. Man, however, is more than an ape with a brilliant mind. His intelligence has carried him so far beyond even the highest primate that finally he seems a creature of a different kind, no longer easily defined as the sum of his biological or mammalian traits, but rather in terms of his actions and their effects on his surroundings. If in this sense he is moving toward the control of his own evolution, it may well be that his next task will be to develop an ethical sense to match and surpass the technological miracles that he has already brought into being, but which do not insure his survival, as man or as mammal.

PEGS OF VARIOUS SHAPES are put in their proper holes in a form board by another hard-working chimpanzee. Because of its more rapid rate of early development and better muscular coordination, a three-year-old chimpanzee will find this task easier to learn than a three-year-old child will.

Bibliography

Biology of Mammals, General

Bourlière, François, *Mammals of the World.* Alfred A. Knopf, 1955. *The Natural History of Mammals.* Alfred A. Knopf, 1954.

Cockrum, E. Lendell, *Introduction to Mammalogy.* Ronald, 1962.

Cott, Hugh B., *Adaptive Coloration in Animals.* Humanities, 1957.

Drimmer, Frederick, ed., *The Animal Kingdom* (Vols. I & II). Greystone Press, 1954.

Hvass, Hans, *Mammals of the World.* Methuen, 1961.

Romer, Alfred S., *The Vertebrate Body* (3rd ed.). Saunders, 1962.

Sanderson, Ivan T., *Living Mammals of the World.* Doubleday, 1955.

Smythe, R. H., *Animal Vision.* Thomas, 1961.

Young, J. Z., *The Life of Mammals.* Oxford University Press, 1957. *The Life of Vertebrates* (2nd ed.). Oxford University Press, 1962.

Classification, Evolution, Fossils

Allen, Glover, *Extinct and Vanishing Mammals of the Western Hemisphere.* American Committee for International Wildlife Protection, 1942.

†Carrington, Richard, *A Guide to Earth History.* New American Library of World Literature, 1961.

*Colbert, Edwin H., *Evolution of the Vertebrates.* John Wiley & Sons, 1955.

Dobzhansky, Theodosius, *Evolution, Genetics and Man.* John Wiley & Sons, 1955.

Dunbar, Carl O., *Historical Geology* (2nd ed.). John Wiley & Sons, 1960.

Flint, Richard F., *Glacial and Pleistocene Geology.* John Wiley & Sons, 1957.

Gregory, William King, *Evolution Emerging* (2 vols.). Macmillan, 1951.

†Harper, Francis, *Extinct and Vanishing Mammals of the Old World.* American Committee for International Wildlife Protection, 1945.

Huxley, Julian, *Evolution: The Modern Synthesis.* Harper & Bros., 1942.

Romer, Alfred S., *Vertebrate Paleontology* (2nd ed.). University of Chicago Press, 1945. *The Vertebrate Story* (4th ed.). University of Chicago Press, 1959.

Scott, William B., *A History of Land Mammals in the Western Hemisphere* (rev. ed.). Hafner, 1962.

Simpson, George Gaylord, **The Meaning of Evolution.* Yale University Press, 1960. †*Principles of Classification and a Classification of Mammals.* American Museum of Natural History, 1945.

Regional Books and Guides

Blair, W. F. (and others), *Vertebrates of the United States.* McGraw-Hill, 1957.

Burt, W. H., and R. P. Grossenheider, *A Field Guide to the Mammals.* Houghton Mifflin, 1952.

Cahalane, Victor H., *Mammals of North America.* Macmillan, 1947.

Carter, T.D., J.E. Hill and G.H.H. Tate, *Mammals of the Pacific World.* Macmillan, 1945.

Hamilton, William John, *American Mammals.* McGraw-Hill, 1939. *The Mammals of Eastern United States.* Comstock Publishing, 1943.

Jackson, Hartley H. T., *The Mammals of Wisconsin.* University of Wisconsin Press, 1961.

Leopold, A. Starker, *Wildlife in Mexico.* University of California Press, 1959.

Matthews, L. Harrison, *British Mammals.* Collins, 1952.

Mochi, Ugo, and T. D. Carter, *Hoofed Mammals of the World.* Scribner, 1953.

Murie, Olaus J., *A Field Guide to Animal Tracks.* Houghton Mifflin, 1954.

National Geographic Book Service, *Wild Animals of North America.* The National Geographic Society, 1960.

Palmer, Ralph S., *The Mammal Guide.* Doubleday, 1954.

Prater, Stanley Henry, *The Book of Indian Animals.* Bombay Natural History Society, 1948.

Schwartz, Charles W. and Elizabeth R., *The Wild Mammals of Missouri.* University of Missouri Press, 1960.

Spinage, C. A., *Animals of East Africa.* Houghton Mifflin, 1963.

Tate, George H. H., *Mammals of Eastern Asia.* Macmillan, 1947.

Troughton, Ellis, *Furred Animals of Australia.* Scribner, 1947.

Specific Mammals

*Allen, Glover, *Bats.* Harvard University Press, 1939. Reprinted by Dover, 1962.

*Carrington, Richard, *Elephants.* Basic Books, 1959.

Crowcroft, Peter, *The Life of the Shrew.* Reinhardt, 1957.

†Fleay, David, *We Breed the Platypus.* Robertson & Mullens, 1944.

Griffin, Donald R., †*Echoes of Bats and Men.* Doubleday, 1960. *Listening in the Dark.* Yale University Press, 1958.

Howell, Alfred Brazier, *Aquatic Mammals.* Thomas, 1930.

Murie, Olaus J., *The Elk of North America.* Wildlife Management Institute and Stackpole Co., 1951.

Rue, Leonard Lee, III, *The World of the White-tailed Deer.* Lippincott, 1962.

Scheffer, Victor B., *Seals, Sea Lions, and Walruses.* Stanford University Press, 1958.

*Simpson, George Gaylord, *Horses.* Oxford University Press, 1951.

Slijper, E. J., *Whales.* Basic Books, 1962.

Young, Stanley P., and Hartley H. T. Jackson, *Clever Coyote.* Stackpole, 1951.

Young, Stanley P., and Edward A. Goldman, *The Wolves of North America.* American Wildlife Institute, 1944.

Man and the Primates

Carpenter, Clarence Ray, *A Field Study of the Behavior and Social Relations of the Howling Monkeys.* Johns Hopkins, 1934.

Clark, W. E. LeGros, **Antecedents of Man.* Harper & Row, 1963. †*History of the Primates.* University of Chicago Press, 1957.

Coon, Carleton S., *The Story of Man* (2nd ed.). Alfred A. Knopf, 1962.

Hayes, Cathy, *The Ape in Our House.* Harper & Row, 1951.

Hill, W. C. Osman, *Man As an Animal.* Hillary House, 1957.

Huxley, Julian, ed., *The Humanist Frame.* Harper & Row, 1962.

*La Barre, Weston, *The Human Animal.* University of Chicago Press, 1960.

†Romer, Alfred S., *Man and the Vertebrates* (2 vols.). Penguin, 1933.

*Teilhard de Chardin, Pierre, *The Phenomenon of Man.* Harper & Row, 1959.

Washburn, Sherwood L., ed., *Social Life of Early Man.* Aldine, 1961.

*Wormington, H., *Ancient Man in North America* (4th ed.). Denver Museum of Natural History, 1957.

Yerkes, Robert M., *Chimpanzees.* Yale University Press, 1943.

Yerkes, Robert M. and A. W., *The Great Apes.* Yale University Press, 1929.

Zuckermann, Solly, *The Social Life of Monkeys and Apes.* Harcourt, Brace, 1932.

Behavior and Communication

*Dethier, Vincent G., and Eliot Stellar, *Animal Behavior.* Prentice-Hall, 1961.

*Kellogg, Winthrop N., *Porpoises and Sonar.* University of Chicago Press, 1961.

*Köhler, Wolfgang, *The Mentality of Apes.* Random House, 1959.

*Scott, John Paul, *Animal Behavior.* Doubleday, 1963.

Thorpe, William H., *Learning and Instinct in Animals.* Harvard University Press, 1956.

Miscellaneous

Darlington, Philip J., Jr., *Zoogeography.* John Wiley & Sons, 1957.

*Gray, James, *How Animals Move.* Cambridge University Press, 1959.

Heape, Walter, *Emigration, Migration and Nomadism.* Heffer, 1931.

Howell, A. Brazier, *Speed in Animals.* University of Chicago Press, 1944.

Kendeigh, S. Charles, *Animal Ecology.* Prentice-Hall, 1961.

Milne, Lorus J. and Margery J., *Paths Across the Earth.* Harper & Bros., 1958.

* Also available in paperback edition.

† Only available in paperback edition.

A Key to North American Mammal Footprints

These footprints of 53 representative North American mammals are all drawn one sixth natural size, except for the bears, which are one eighth natural size. Where two prints are given for a single animal, the upper one is for the front foot, the lower one for the hind foot. Tracks vary from animal to animal, depending on age, sex, size and weight of the individual. Those shown here are for average specimens, and this is how they would look if made in mud—all but the polar bear and snowshoe hare, which are shown as they would look in snow. Seldom do prints as clear as these occur in nature, but if several impressions from a single animal are examined, they usually add up to an identifiable print.

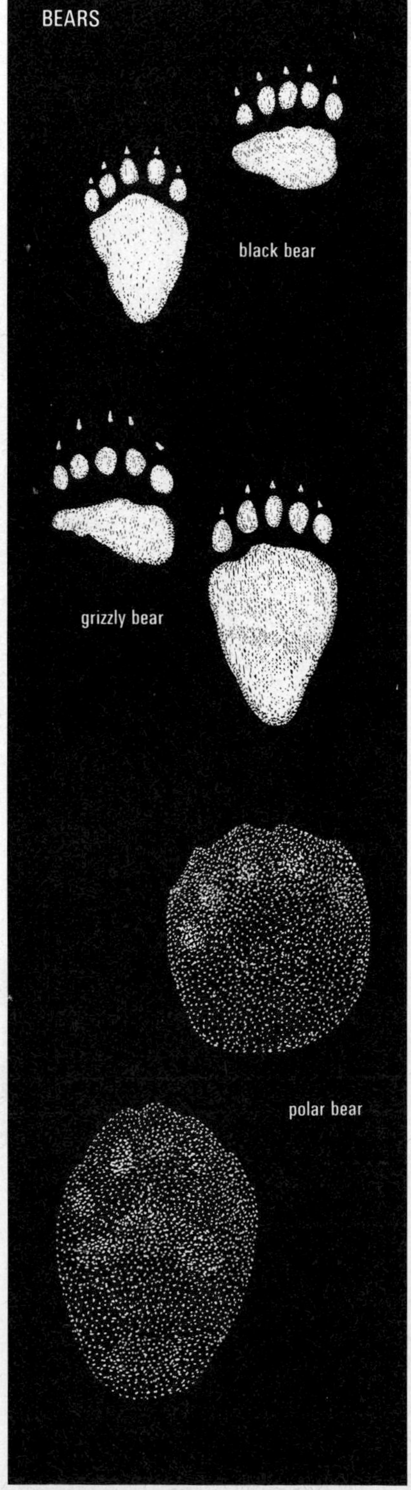

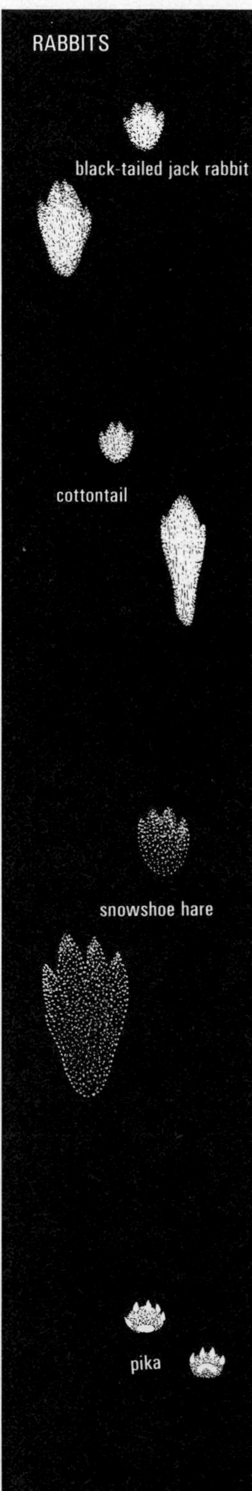

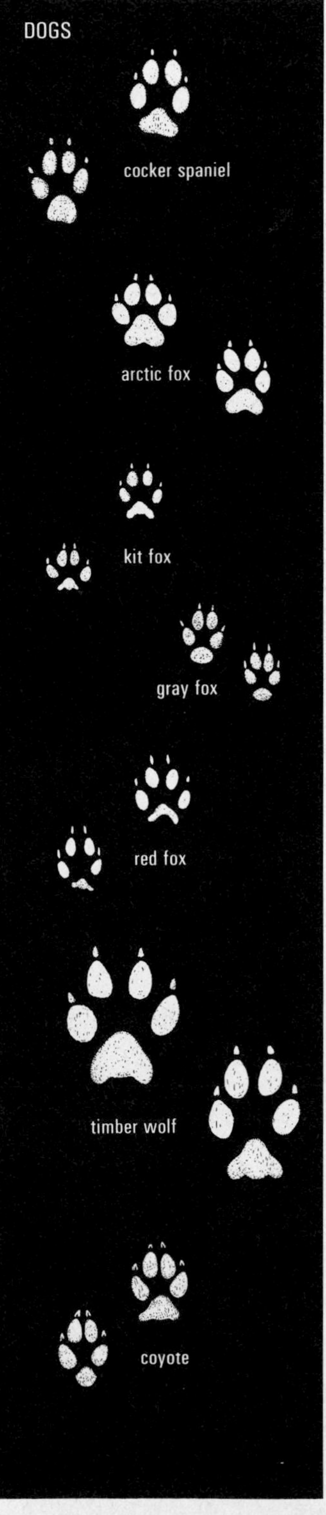

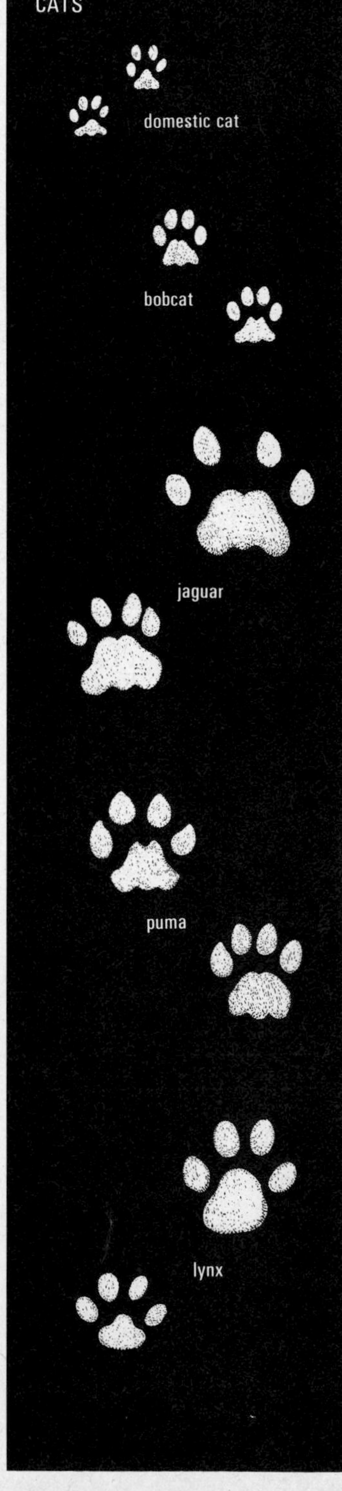

When an animal is running fast its prints are usually larger and deeper than when it is walking. Identification is complicated among many species by the fact that the hind prints are superimposed on the front ones.

Prints fall into three main classes. First are those of the plantigrade animals, the deliberate-moving bears, raccoons, badgers, porcupines and beavers, which walk flat-footed with their heels touching the ground. Next come the swifter digitigrade animals, like cats and dogs, which stand on their toes and whose heels do not touch the ground. Finally come the unguligrades, the deer, goats, horses and others, which actually stand on the tips of their toenails.

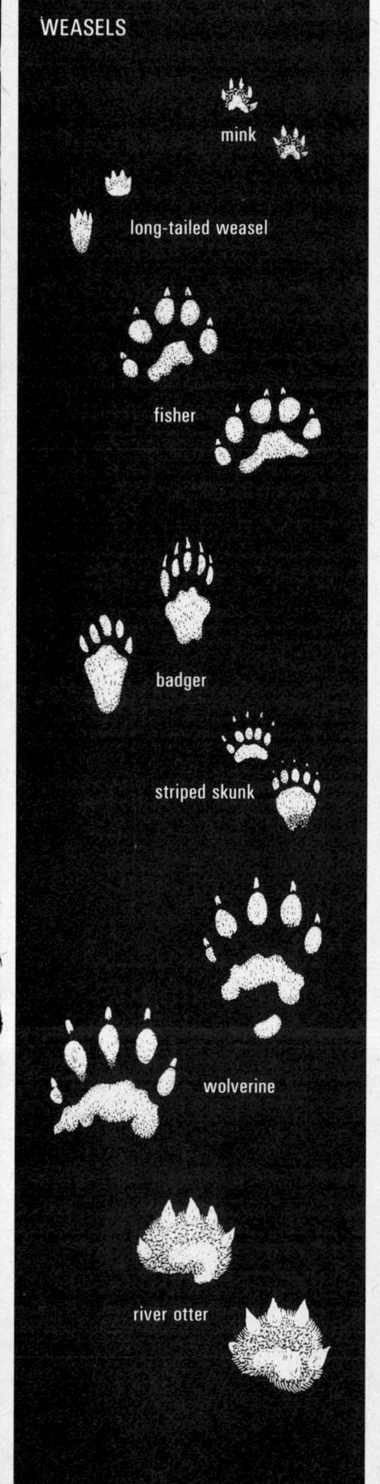

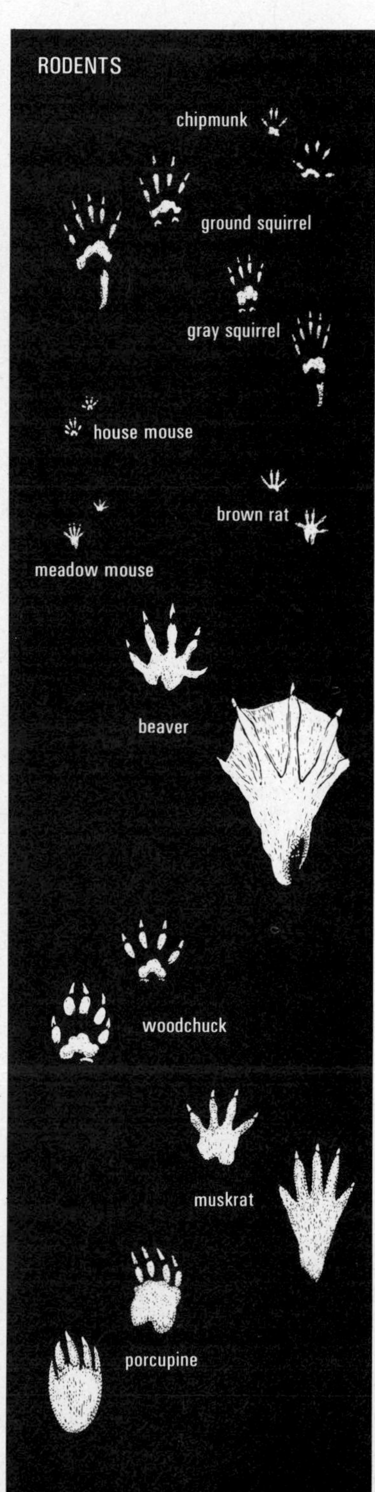

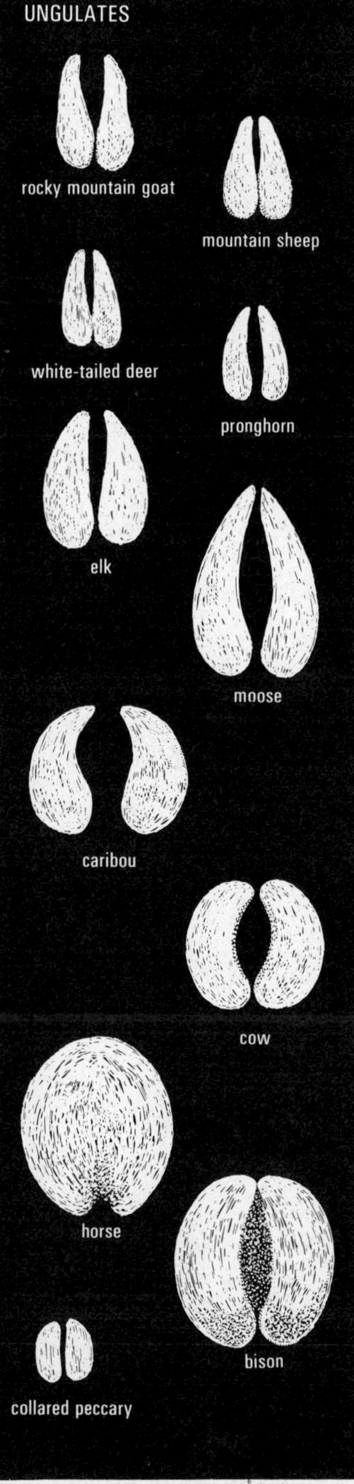

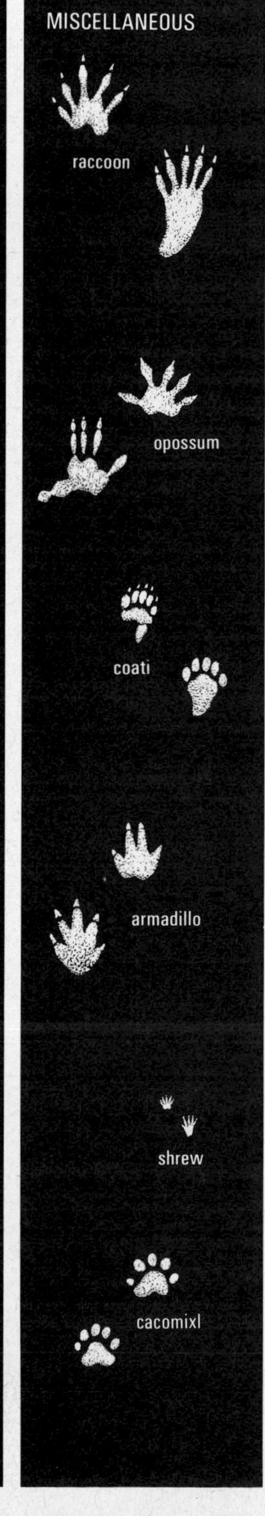

Credits

The sources for the illustrations in this book are shown below.

Credits for pictures from left to right are separated by commas, top to bottom by dashes.

Cover—Nina Leen
8,9—Paul Popper, Ltd.
10,11—drawings by Lowell Hess
12,13—drawings by Rudolf Freund
14,15—drawings by Hans Zillessen
17—drawings by Rudolf Freund
19—Wallace Kirkland
20,21—drawings by Rene Martin
22,23—drawings by Jean Zallinger
24—Andreas Feininger
25—Shelly Grossman
26—Lewis W. Walker, Arizona Sonora Desert Museum
27—Sven Gillsäter
28,29—Emil Schulthess from Black Star—Sven Gillsäter
30,31—George Leavens from Photo Researchers, Inc., Jack Dermid
32,33—George Silk
34—Jean B. Thorpe
36—drawing by Adolph E. Brotman
37 through 41—drawings by Rudolf Freund
43—Romain Robert
44 through 47—paintings by Joseph Cellini
48,49,50—paintings by Walter Ferguson
51—Helmut Heimpel
52,53—drawing by Joseph Cellini
54—Jürg Klages
56,57—drawings by Eva Cellini
58—drawings by Betty Davis
63,64,65—Andreas Feininger
66—Sam Shere, Russ Kinne from Photo Researchers, Inc.—New York Zoological Society
67—Aldo Margiocco
68—Professor Dr. Bernhard Grzimek, George Leavens from Photo Researchers, Inc.—Julien Bryan from Photo Researchers, Inc.
70—top David Goodnow; bottom Shelly Grossman
71—top David Goodnow; bottom Shelly Grossman
72,73—painting by Rudolf Freund
74—Wallace Kirkland
77—drawings by Hans Zillessen
78—drawings by Eva Cellini
80,81—drawings by Rudolf Freund
83—Maitland A. Edey
84—B. H. Reed from Annan Photo Features
85—Aldo Margiocco from Paul Popper, Ltd.—Carl Iwasaki
86,87—Baron Hans von Meiss-Teuffen from Photo Researchers, Inc., Emil Schulthess from Black Star, Commander Gatti from Free Lance Photographers Guild
88,89—Dale A. Zimmerman, Bruce Hayward—Dale A. Zimmerman, Bruce Hayward, Mervin Larson, Bruce Hayward
90—Francois Merlet
91—Dale A. Zimmerman, Karl Maslowski from Photo Researchers, Inc.—Andreas Feininger—Leonard Lee Rue III from Annan Photo Features
92,93—left George Santillo from Rapho-Guillumette—Russ Kinne from Photo Researchers, Inc.; right Russ Kinne from Photo Researchers, Inc.—Pierre Marc—Lois Crisler
94—left Ed Cesar from Annan Photo Features; right Leonard Lee Rue III from National Audubon Society
95—Karl Maslowski from Photo Researchers, Inc.
96—Fritz Goro
98,99—drawings by Rudolf Freund
100—drawing by Eva Cellini
101—drawings by Mark A. Binn
102,103—drawings by Rudolf Freund
105—Ylla from Rapho-Guillumette
106,107—L. David Mech
108—Lois Crisler
109—Ed Cesar from Annan Photo Features
110,111—top Mrs. Peter Molloy; bottom Mrs. H. Stevenson-Hamilton from Frank W. Lane
112,113—top Shelly Grossman; bottom Lynwood M. Chase
114—Eric H. Hosking
115—W. Suschitzky
116,117—William Vandivert
118—Ylla from Rapho-Guillumette for SPORTS ILLUSTRATED except top left Ylla from Rapho-Guillumette
119—Ylla from Rapho-Guillumette for SPORTS ILLUSTRATED
120—Karl W. Kenyon
122,123—drawing by Lowell Hess
126—drawing by Adolph E. Brotman—drawing by Mark A. Binn
127—drawing by Adolph E. Brotman—drawing by Mark A. Binn
129,130,131—Charles J. Ott from National Audubon Society
132—Charles E. Mohr from National Audubon Society
133—Professor C. G. Hampson
134—Francois Merlet
135—Eric H. Hosking—Ed Park, Leonard Lee Rue III from Annan Photo Features
136—Wayne Replogle, Photo Researchers, Inc.—Ed Cesar from Annan Photo Features (2), R. H. Hooke from National Audubon Society, Leonard Lee Rue III from Annan Photo Features
138—William Vandivert
139—Jack Dermid
140—Morgan and Swan from Free Lance Photographers Guild
142,143—drawings by Rudolf Freund
145—drawing by Eric Gluckman
146,147—drawings by Betty Davis
151—David Goodnow
152,153—Pete Turner from Free Lance Photographers Guild—William W. Bacon III from Rapho-Guillumette, George Silk
154,155—William Vandivert
156—Janet E. R. Finch from Annan Photo Features
157—Jürg Klages from Black Star
158,159—Lynwood M. Chase, Werner Haller from Zoological Garden, Zurich, Dr. U. Rahm courtesy Institute for Scientific Research in Central Africa—W. Suschitzky, William Vandivert—Dr. Hanna-Maria Zippelius
160,161—London Daily Express
162—William Vandivert
163—Charles Philip Fox
164—W. Suschitzky
166,167—drawings by Lois and Louis Darling
168—drawing by Lowell Hess
170—drawings by Lowell Hess
173—Nina Leen
174—Walter Dawn
175—Dmitri Kessel
176—Ylla from Rapho-Guillumette
177,178—W. Suschitzky
179—Ylla from Rapho-Guillumette
180—top Mark Kauffman; bottom Dr. Keith J. Hayes (2), Mark Kauffman
182,183—Lilo Hess
184,185—drawings by John Norris Wood
Back cover—Matt Greene

Acknowledgments

The editors of this book are particularly indebted to Richard G. Van Gelder, Chairman, and Sydney Anderson, Assistant Curator, Department of Mammalogy, The American Museum of Natural History, who read the book in its entirety. The editors are also indebted to François Bourlière, Faculté de Médecine de Paris; Edwin H. Colbert, Chairman, Department of Vertebrate Paleontology, The American Museum of Natural History; Lee Crandall, General Curator Emeritus, and J. A. Davis Jr., Curator of Mammals, New York Zoological Society; Joseph L. Evans, Assistant Professor of Nutrition, Rutgers University; Reed W. Fautin, Professor of Zoology, University of Wyoming; John N. Hamlet; S. Charles Kendeigh, Professor of Zoology, University of Illinois; Richard Klein, Curator of Plant Physiology, New York Botanical Garden; L. Harrison Matthews, Scientific Director, Zoological Society of London; Malcolm C. McKenna, Assistant Curator, Department of Vertebrate Paleontology, The American Museum of Natural History; Frank A. Pitelka, Professor of Zoology, University of California, Berkeley; Richard G. Zweifel, Curator, Department of Herpetology, and the library staff, The American Museum of Natural History.

Index

Numerals in italics indicate a photograph or painting of the subject mentioned.

PRODUCTION STAFF FOR TIME INCORPORATED

John L. Hallenbeck (Vice President and Director of Production), Robert E. Foy and Caroline Ferri

Text photocomposed under the direction of Albert J. Dunn